From Winchester to This

From Winchester to This

William Donaldson

PETER OWEN
London & Chester Springs

PETER OWEN PUBLISHERS
73 Kenway Road, London SW5 0RE
Peter Owen books are distributed in the USA by
Dufour Editions Inc., Chester Springs, PA 19425–0007

First published in Great Britain 1998
© William Donaldson 1998

ISBN 0 7206 1063 X

A catalogue record for this book is available from the British Library

Printed and bound in Great Britain by
Redwood Books, Trowbridge, Wiltshire

The extracts from *The Human Province* by Elias Canetti
are reproduced with the kind permission of André Deutsch Ltd

Lunch at the Ivy with the Publisher. As usual, I arrive on time – this habit of punctuality being a necessary condition, I think, of my addiction, first noticed when I was researching *Root Into Europe* in 1990. After a mere three weeks away, bucketing round France, Italy and Spain with Mark Chapman, Jeremy Lovering and Justin Judd, my withdrawal symptoms were appalling.

More interesting, I think, than the usual ones – cold sweats, sleeplessness, loss of concentration – was this awesome punctuality, which was in such sharp contrast to my three colleagues' flaky inability to know what time or even what day it was (being alive now, they called it), and was – is – a function not, as I used to suppose, of my naval background but of a crushing boredom with the present, an addict's agitated need to press on to the next stage, whatever horrors might there unfold.

I wait for the Publisher, order an unaccustomed brandy and sink into my past. I used to come to the Ivy when I put on plays. I winged a few pigeons here in my day, once, with both barrels, brought down David Jacobs, the theatrical solicitor. I took him for £10,000, and the next time I saw him I, through some confusion in my career, was Mr Grant the Visiting Masseur, and he was Mr Howard, wishing, in an afternoon flat and for £5 only, to be rebuked by a therapist as pseudonymous as himself.

I don't know which of us was more surprised, but Mrs Mouse, to whom I was married at the time and who hadn't much cared for my previous occupation (teaching English Literature at an A-level crammer in Maida Vale), was proud of me for bringing home the bacon.

Potential investors liked the Ivy's atmosphere, I think. They liked the heavy furniture, the old-time waiters, the numinous presence of Jack Hulbert and Cicely Courtneidge, of Binkie and Bottom and Binnie and Boo, the present possibility that Robert Morley and Coral Browne, Dame Moira Lister and 'Tim' Hardy might be lunching to left and right. I once abandoned Moira Lister in Liverpool and without her train fare back to London, and she's still going on about it twenty years later.

They liked the food, too, I think, the potential investors. Entrecôte the old way, nothing silly, and your choice cooked almost to a standard which might have been achieved at home – even by me, and I can't cook at all.

I should have visited the Ivy when I was *Tatler*'s restaurant critic under Tina Brown and when, since it didn't cross my mind that even a *Tatler* reader would care what another person had for lunch, I ignored the food and instead discussed what a range of 'companions' – novelists, women, criminals, TV people – might be up to at the moment. As a result, the restaurants all withdrew their advertising, but Tina told them to sit on it.

It's all different now, of course – the upshot, I believe, of its having been taken over by the two go-getters who recently did a job on the Caprice, another former haunt of mine. The food now is fashionably simple (fishcakes and so forth), food on the go, as it were, food in the fast lane, clever food rather to the taste of the serious young players here to pitch – though less so, I imagine, to the sprinkling of people who, sadly, were someone once but who now are calamitously out of it – smooth-faced old parties with manicures and haircuts but with terror in their eyes.

I recognize one of them, I think, a *farceur* from the old days trying to sell something to a scornful boy. The scornful boy will smell the fear and send the *farceur* packing. He shouldn't be here at all, the manicured *farceur*. He should be at home, screaming solitary insults at a daytime TV screen.

Only the confidence born of inherited wealth would confound this insolent youth – according, at least, to a story recently passed on by Pete the Schnoz. Pete the Schnoz had been lunching at the Kensington Place Restaurant when John Birt was hit full in the face by a flying sea bass.

The Kensington Place, according to Pete the Schnoz, is the

preferred meeting-ground of Filofaxes on the make, serious haircuts pitching and lying to one another from behind shades reflecting the *vis-à-vis*. Pitch it wrong, commit yourself to words, which, in your frenzy to impress, you can't pronounce, and you could be on the skids before the artichokes arrive; at best, out of the business altogether; at worst, directing corporate videos or writing jokes for *Have I Got News For You.*

To gain entry, according to Pete the Schnoz, you must first fax your credits to a pony-tailed *maitre d'* and, even then, if admitted, the easily intimidated can, on stepping inside, be washed back on to the street by a tidal wave of sheer achievement.

'You'll get the picture,' said Pete the Schnoz. 'Jeremy Paxman passing between tables, Yentob in conference with Birt, a boy film director who's so hot they're catching a tan at the next table, another who's so *globally* hot that they're waking up with tans in Japan.'

Pete the Schnoz, unusually for a writer as good as he is, has a vigorous conversational style.

'Why, then, the flying sea bass?' I asked.

It seems that a party of genetically challenged aristocrats from Gloucestershire had been ignorant and vicious enough to choose this, of all places, to celebrate the twenty-first birthday of Hugo – seemingly, but only by a short head, the most oafish of their number.

They'd booked two tables, according to Pete the Schnoz, with the grown-ups, as it were, at one and the children at the other, and the most you could say for the former, apart from looking as if they belonged in a stable, was that they were a shade less loutish than the latter.

The girls, who had put their car keys on the table next to their Marlboro cigarettes, were more or less identical, according to Pete the Schnoz, with callous little faces and voices like seagulls after a herring catch, but the boys came in two varieties: half of them were fat and bald with food down their fronts and the other half were unnecessarily tall, with floppy hair and careless, cherry-pink mouths.

'We ignored them,' said Pete the Schnoz, 'until Birt was hit full in the face with a flying sea bass. It was extraordinary. The room was stiff with achievement, but these well-born herberts were behaving as if unaware that they were in a public place. You'd have expected them to be thrown out, but the *maitre d'*, who had once refused Michael Grade a table on the grounds that his CV wasn't up to scratch, merely retrieved the sea bass and ordered up another one for Hugo.

'And when Hugo challenged Birt to three games of "Are You There, Moriarty?" Birt meekly acquiesced. Further, when Hugo removed his blindfold, thus ensuring that the still unsighted Birt flailed away at empty air while he, Hugo, caught Birt with three shots which would have dropped a water buffalo, the media hotshots led the laughter. You can't beat old money.'

Nor you can. There's a paradox of some sort here, however, and one which I may, or may not, have brought to Pete the Schnoz's attention at the time. In his interesting book, *Constructions* – a collection of loosely philosophical reflections – Michael Frayn has the following entry:

27. The secret police arrest us all. I, who have been a well-mannered and amusing guest at your dinner-parties these past ten years, betray you as soon as the secret police produce the electrodes. That bore Puling refuses, heroically. If ever we all get out again, don't make the mistake of asking him to your dinner-parties instead of me.

Equally, had the Kensington Place suddenly been taken over by the secret police and the electrodes produced, it's very possible that Hugo and his boorish friends might have stacked up better than the assembled media hotshots.

'When the torpedoes are running, background counts,' as I used to say to Chapman and Lovering, when, during the recce for *Root*

Into Europe, I tried to explain my preference for Justin Judd's company over theirs. I wasn't calling Chapman and Lovering common, although they were, I was merely pointing out that when your backs are against the wall it's best to be with your own kind.

Not that your own kind always make it. I had lunch with my friend Tim Williamson, here at the Ivy, on the very day he came unstuck. Tim dealt drugs to Princess Margaret's friends, but this was just a front from behind which he was married to Sir Robert Mark's daughter and ran an artistes' agency representing Peter Bowles and others.

One day Timmy was as sane as me and the next he walked into the Ivy backwards and padlocked his briefcase to the table-leg. It contained everything he might need in an emergency, he said – a packet of Daz, a roll of lavatory paper and the deeds to his house in Kentish Town. His wife, Christina, he said, might try to seize the latter in his absence but would be confounded if the title deeds were padlocked to a table-leg. Further, his father-in-law, Sir Robert Mark, had taken to following him around in a police helicopter.

Then, fearful that the people lunching to left and right might be police informers, he took the packet of Daz and the roll of lavatory paper out of his briefcase, placed them on the table and insisted that, for the rest of lunch, we communicate by writing messages to each other on the lavatory paper. What the packet of Daz was for I never did discover.

It isn't much fun when a close friend comes unstuck, and when, over the next few weeks, Timmy's symptoms became worse (he thought he had the power to stop buses and proved the point more than once by stepping suddenly into the street in front of one) I did what anyone in my position would have done: I arranged to get my stuff in future from Andy From The Sixties, and I advised Princess Margaret's friends to do the same, which, indeed, they did. So that was all right – at least for me and Princess Margaret's friends, if not for Tim or Andy From The Sixties (who later got sent down for eight years and without Princess Margaret's friends speaking up in his defence).

Timmy went to live with a maiden aunt in Barnes and one day he killed himself with an overdose of Valium. Not much of a life, really – representing Peter Bowles, being followed everywhere by a helicopter piloted by Sir Robert Mark, ending up with an aunt in Barnes. A pretty frightful one, in fact.

I'm musing along these lines, here at the Ivy, when the Publisher arrives. He's good news, the Publisher, if a little hard to place. For one thing, he must be forty-three or so, which is an odd age from where I'm sitting, being neither here nor there; more accurately, perhaps, an age at which you've either obviously made it or you haven't.

Not that the Publisher would see it like this, I think. He's sensibly poised, rather reassuring, neither squinting with ambition nor obviously out of it. He's neutral, would in the war of the flying sea bass, like myself, be on neither side; equally, and, like myself, might find himself in no man's land between the old *farceur*'s position and that of the scornful boy who's taking him for lunch.

That said, and unusually among publishers (who aren't, as a rule, much interested in books these days), his comments always carry weight. I'd rather have lunch with him than with a thin rude woman who has speared her way to the top of a recently conglomerated house.

He takes me by surprise, however, when he suddenly asks me how my memoirs are progressing. He commissioned these some years ago, and my reluctance to deliver, or even to make a start on them, doesn't particularly arise, I think, from any desire to gain a pecuniary advantage or an interest-free loan. It's a reluctance, merely, to write about myself – this diffidence being a consequence of my background. I was brought up to believe that it's bad manners to 'take oneself too seriously', to indulge in sordid introspection or embarrass others with personal disclosures. In Sunningdale, and later at Winchester, we squared the shoulders and cracked on. We didn't dwell.

I've got the anecdotes, of course, but I've done most of them already, some more than once; the Albery tea-party with the cast of *Beyond the Fringe* several times, in fact. Shortly after the show opened in May 1961, Cook, Bennett, Miller and Moore caught on to the fact that while each of them was receiving precisely £75 a week the producers – Sir Donald Albery and myself – were pocketing £2,000 every Friday. This didn't seem equitable, so in due course they wrote courteously to the management, seeking an adjustment.

Sir Donald, whose contribution to the show's success had been to attend the dress-rehearsal (after which he had suggested that 'the one in spectacles should be replaced'), invited them to tea. Over seed cake and Earl Grey he patiently explained the economics of the theatre. 'Difficult times . . . rising costs . . . laundry . . . back and front . . . bricks and mortar . . . the successes have to pay for the flops . . . review the situation when I return from Juan Les Pins in late September . . . have another cup of tea.'

Decisively out-argued – in spite of the intellectual, to say nothing of the moral, disproportion in the room – and having just been told that they were paying for Sir Donald's frightful fucking flops, Miller and Co. retired in confusion and Sir Donald and I ('Nothing I can do . . . over a barrel . . . hands tied . . . so sorry') struggled along on £2,000 a week, but only for the moment. When the show moved to New York we did a great deal better.

I now surprise myself, however, and the Publisher, too, I think, by producing an idea off the top of my head – more accurately, an idea off the top of Jeremy Lovering's head. Lovering was the travelling new man on *Root Into Europe* and keeper of our collective moral conscience. When we held various minority groups up to primetime ridicule Lovering preferred to stay indoors, washing his hair and ironing his shirts. In the course of the recce for *Root Into Europe*, and while we enjoyed a short break in Mark Chapman's property in the

Dordogne, Lovering asked me one day how my memoirs were progressing.

'I'm blocked,' I'd said. 'I can't find a decent voice to do them in. I'm not accustomed to writing about myself.'

'You never write about anything else,' he'd said.

Which showed, I suppose, how wise he had been to choose a career in television rather than in literary journalism. The narrator of my stuff is – obviously, I'd have thought – as much a 'character' as any of the others; he and the nervous, once-a-week style being simply the consequence of an embarrassed inability to write a straightforward sentence and both, equally, inappropriate in memoirs.

'Here's an idea,' Lovering had continued. 'You and I go round the world together – the old gun and the young Turk – sharing a number of strange adventures. In the course of these I try to impress you with my moral and intellectual vigour; you me with the lessons learnt in a long life. Action in the present explained by senescent *racontage*. I *do*, you try to slow me down with interminable reminiscence, to entangle me in a web of cautionary anecdotes – the lessons learnt in a long life. You have learnt some lessons, I suppose?'

'Just one,' I'd said. 'Not to put the seals on first. If you put the seals on first the stage thereafter will be as slippery as an ice-rink. In *Nights at the Comedy*, my attempt to revive music hall in the West End, I put the seals on first. Ida Barr, on next, aged eighty-six and singing "The Boy I Love Is Up in the Gallery", went head over heels into the orchestra stalls.'

'There you are,' Lovering had said. 'Your first burst of *racontage* already. We're up and running here.'

I now pass this idea on to the Publisher as mine.

'The past and the present side by side,' I say. 'How the retributive nature of one's biography bears down on the present, forming and transforming it. A volume of memoirs done as *racontage* to a second party, or parties, sharing current escapades. From Winchester to this.'

12

'I'm sorry?' says the Publisher.

I explain that this will be the title; that my strategy will be to blame the past for present mishaps; that I'll blame my parents (a socially rampant mother, a gentle but alcoholic father), Mr Emmett, my housemaster at Winchester, Pode, the head of house, my naval training, my formidable sister Bobo, Aunt Margot, the Pinkneys (Daph and Gee) with whom, in Sunningdale, on late September evenings my mother and father played tennis in the softening light, while I lay awake in one of our home's twenty-seven bedrooms, each with bath *en suite*.

'Small wonder I've had my ups and downs,' I say. 'Each event will trigger a volley of reminiscence; the recipient of this a helpless stooge or straight man.'

'It sounds as if . . .'

Listen. None of it's my fault. When I was ten my mother engaged George Geary of Leicestershire and England to coach me at cricket in the holidays. He was a fine old boy with weatherbeaten country ways and shoulders as wide as a barn door. He called me 'Master William' and I called him 'Geary' and at lunchtime we went our separate ways, I to be waited on by the butler in the dining-room, he to the servants' hall.

Not my fault, do you see? And in the grounds there was a lake which had moorhens on it. When I was eleven I was kitted out by my mother in plus-fours identical to my father's and equipped with a twelve-bore too. Since it was as big as I was, its kick when I let it off lifted me twenty yards backwards into a ditch, but I mastered it in time and, dressed in plus-fours identical to my father's, I crept up behind the moorhens and blew them to bits.

Most crucially, when I was thirteen, I persuaded my parents to take me to see the *Folies Bergère*, then visiting London. I was enthralled. I understood immediately that these tall silent women pacing the stage with nothing on – so different to anything one saw in Sunningdale – were the self-evidently desirable representatives of their sex since men would pay to see them with nothing on.

There was no one in Sunningdale you'd pay to see with nothing on. I smuggled the souvenir programme back to Winchester and gazed at it in private, from then on confusing pleasure with vaguely illicit displays of nudity for cash down – a confusion very powerfully reinforced when the souvenir programme was confiscated by my housemaster, Mr Emmett, and I was thrashed for immorality by Pode, the head of house.

Yet when I had a love affair with a boy named Law, now a judge, Mr Emmett smiled, not unkindly, and passed me up the line to his celebrated predecessor, Harry Altham, co-author, with E. W. 'Jim' Swanton, of *The History of Cricket* and Secretary in his day of the MCC. Harry A, as he was known, invited me and Law to tea, encouraged us to rehearse for his benefit the details of our affair, pulled deeply on his pipe, spoke of the Greeks and sent us on our way.

I'm not criticizing Harry A – merely pointing out some disproportion in the punishments at Winchester for dreaming about girls and doing it with boys. Small wonder that in later life I set up house with civilian girls but, for pleasure, preferred a transaction unpermitted by Pode and Mr Emmett: an arrangement with a silent performing woman in a service flat, a woman for a living, as it were.

'Surely there were some good influences? George Geary must have been a wise old bird. He never tried to knock your block off? Did no one try to help?'

Only Julian Mitchell, who was a friend of mine at Winchester and later in the Navy. On leave from the Navy he and I visited Paris and picked up two tarts behind the Opéra. Mine was patient enough, as I recall (bearing in mind that her client's only previous experience had been with Law, now a judge) but the experiment wasn't a great success.

Apart from that, Julian did his best; he gave me books to read, drew my attention to art and so on, insisted, when the Navy let us, that we visit galleries and concerts, the Edinburgh Festival and so forth. The damage was already done, however. I quite took to the ballet, as it happens, but only, I think, because I greatly admired Svetlana Beriosova, then at the start of a brilliant career.

Rather than miss her first Aurora or Odette/Odile, and being in the Navy at the time, I would drive by Daimler Hire from my barracks in Portsmouth to Covent Garden where, dressed in my sailor suit and while my chauffeur waited outside, I'd mingle in the Crush Bar, causing more than one old ballet buff to take a step back and sit on his opera hat – not least Dickie Buckle, who wrote to me thereafter, addressing me as 'Dear Mr Midshipman Clever . . .' and inviting me to tea.

My interest lay elsewhere, however. I rocked gently in my hammock, dreaming of Miss Beriosova, and when the curtain fell on her Aurora or Odette/Odile, and while others offered floral tributes, I, or if I was at sea, an authorized representative, showered the stage with jewellery and share certificates – a habit which, on one occasion, caused my father some embarrassment.

Miss Beriosova rang me up in Sunningdale and, assuming that there was only one Mr Donaldson at this address, thanked my father for the gift of a diamond bracelet. For some reason my father didn't tell me about this at the time. My Uncle Hal told me some years later, after my father had died. My father had been confused, perhaps, but relieved too, I imagine, that I was apparently heading in the right direction – albeit as a punter. He had been a trifle concerned by my friendship with Julian Mitchell – his fears having been aroused by a postcard, depicting Michelangelo's David, which Julian had sent from Italy. Judging this obscene, my father had confiscated it and, like his conversation with Miss Beriosova, I found out about it only after his death.

'A blizzard of *racontage*, do you see? The recipient, a helpless stooge or straight man.'

'Interesting,' says the Publisher. 'When can you start?'

'I've already started. This is it.'

The Publisher registers a flicker of concern. 'I'm in? Cannon to your Ball already?'

'In a nutshell.'

I then decide to elicit his help in solving a current problem. For some time I have been keen to acquire a copy of Stevie Wonder's excellent hit song of 1985, 'I Just Called to Say I Love You'. Aware that a man of a certain age, dressed in a John Lewis Partnership blazer, would be unable to seek this out in a record shop without attracting a degree of ridicule from the multi-pierced youth behind the counter, I have asked various of my young friends to get it for me. None has so far obliged.

'Would you purchase on my behalf,' I say, 'Stevie Wonder's hit single "I Just Called to Say I Love You"? It has nostalgic associations to do with Ibiza in 1985 and Melanie and . . .'

The Publisher blanches, rather as my mother used to blanch when I discovered at the age of three that I could cause the world to make no sense to her by saying 'Pardon?' in the presence of Lady Mary Burghley.

'Excuse me,' he says. 'There's someone over there I must have a word with. I'll be back in a moment.'

At first I think I've blown it, that this glimpse of my musical taste has caused the Publisher to judge that my memoirs may not be at the cutting edge of chic. But then I think, don't panic, he'll be back, and I sink again into private reminiscence – realizing soon enough that I could have passed on to young Lovering a lesson of more general application than not to put the seals on first.

To succeed in life, I could have said, you must delay for as long as possible the moment when you suddenly say, 'Never mind – it's all bollocks anyway' – not least if you're the man in charge. Others on an enterprise lose heart if the man in charge suddenly sees the joke.

Justin Judd suddenly, and disastrously, saw the joke during the shoot of *Root Into Europe*, and he was the producer, the man we looked to for *esprit* and attitude and so forth. Chapman, Lovering and I were sitting outside a Spanish café, our little faces tense with primetime artistic ambition, when Judd, the producer, could contain himself no longer.

'Never mind – it's all bollocks anyway!' he said.

I rocked with silly laughter and fell instantly in love, but the others were confused. Nor did it escape me that if Judd wants, in the long run, to be obviously successful he'll have to keep on a leash this very natural desire to kick the table over when in charge. It won't be easy for someone as thoughtful as he is, but I think he'll manage.

So far so good, I think. The past and the present side by side. I'll concoct a fictional escapade (myself and a young Turk locked in a deadly game: he trying to annihilate me with his moral and intellectual vigour; I him with narcoleptic anecdotes) into which the past – intruding as a blizzard of *racontage* – will collide as a limiting influence.

And now I have another thought. Perhaps I'll do it as a diary. People are at ease with diaries. Nice short sentences. Nice short entries. 'Ah – here's one. Not too much of a mouthful at this time of night. I'll sample this one.' Bang, you fall instantly asleep. It doesn't matter in the least. No complicated plot to follow or cast of characters to distinguish. You can start at any point.

There's the bonus, too, that because of the casual, last-thing-at-night nature of the jottings (the impression being that they have been tipped on to the page while the malicious judgements are still hot and unedited in the mind) readers suppose, I think, that what they have before them must be true.

Which isn't to say that what I write won't, when I start the thing, be true. On the contrary. And this, I think, is where the diary form may help most crucially – solving the problem of embarrassment by emphasizing rather than by removing it. When reading unserious non-fiction – the memoirs of a dirty politician, the confessions of

Lady Geldof – one quite likes to be embarrassed, to feel that one is about to be told too much; one quite likes to wince and look away and then to peep again; one is quite gripped, actually, by someone revealing too much, by something uncontrolled; one is grateful in a way for this lack of judgement, this failure of decorum.

That, in any case, is how I'll do it. As a diary. Nice short entries. Nice short sentences. The honesty secured by brevity.

Thus:

SUNDAY. The anxiety persists. It must be forty years since a ring at the front door didn't terrify me. It must be odd not to jump every time the doorbell goes. We didn't, as I recall, jump like salmon when the doorbell rang in Sunningdale. The butler answered it, I think.

TUESDAY. Tea with Drummond. A shade less obviously mad than he was at Cambridge. He reports that Bremner has come a cropper.

WEDNESDAY. Lunch with Watty. He tells me that a smart bald fuck called Jacques has taken over the Comment pages of the *Independent*. He sees no future for my column.

THURSDAY. Tea with Frankie Fraser. He's a diamond, Frank. He's got a bit of a temper on him, he lets himself down a couple of times a year, but Jacques and his sort are shits from soup to nuts.

That sort of stuff. Nice short entries. Nice short sentences. The malice excused by the need to excel at point of sale. I'll start immediately.

A minor worry now intrudes. Can I be bothered to concoct a fictional escapade? Obviously not, I think – but without one will I have enough material? I'm not short of *racontage*, but, without invention, do I achieve enough from day to day to balance the present with the past? These days, after all, leaving the flat is – in so far as this is possible – something I avoid.

Except with Penny, my beloved. With her I'd dine at Le Gavroche. I'd go to a football match with her or to an *opéra bouffe*. With her I'd attend a publishing party at the Groucho Club, balance a glass and listen to a wizened mad woman in an ethnic dress. I'd go into a pub with her or to a society wedding on an English lawn. I'd go to Somerset with her.

Happily, she wants to do none of these things, so, fortified by a water-pipe and a Bunsen burner, we stay indoors and satirize reality. Since I have no other social life – least of all with young Turks of Lovering's sort – I'll be obliged to tell my anecdotes to her. Most of my memoirs will take place in the course of a long drug-fuelled conversation with Penny, my beloved.

The first chunk will start in a page or two. Meanwhile, and for construction's sake (I need something to happen in the present), Mark Chapman telephones to say that Central Television want to commission a *Root* special, to be set in England and shot next year.

'Who would you like to write it with?' asks Chapman.

I have a theory (and this, perhaps, is the lesson I should have passed on to young Lovering, rather than not to put the seals on first) that one should only work with people who are obviously cleverer than you are.

'Pete the Schnoz,' I say.

I've not seen the Schnoz's stuff, in fact, but, judging by his own account of it, it must be very good indeed. In any case, he's obviously cleverer than me and thus, by my own theory, I should work with him.

'OK,' says Chapman. 'Talk to him about it. Where is he at the moment?'

'In Rome, I think, working on a Spike Jones film. I'll mention it to him when he gets back.'

In fact, Pete the Schnoz is on holiday in Bangkok with Cathy, his beloved, but I judged that Chapman would be more impressed to hear that he was working with Spike Jones. He might have been even more impressed had I said – which I had intended – Spike Lee, or even Mike Leigh, but one of Chapman's many admirable characteristics is never to draw attention to unimportant gaffes. He would never have embarrassed me by pointing out that Spike Jones once fronted a slapstick band trading as Spike Jones and the City Slickers. Anyway, this is exciting news, the best aspect being that with the fees I'll receive from Central Television I'll be able to spoil my baby.

Some addicts can instantly compute their disposable incomes, normal utilities and dry goods on offer in terms of grams ('A new electric kettle? Are you insane? That's half a gram of Peruvian pink!'). I can compute mine in terms of surprises for my baby ('Five thousand pounds from Central Television? That's a Valentino suit, a Versace frock, two blouses from Agnès B and a pair of Chanel earrings').

Accordingly, and having done the instant calculation in my head, I set forth now on a small shopping spree in Knightsbridge, thinking as I hurry from shop to shop that, whatever the down-side of addiction is, I'll say this for my condition: it isn't boring and, almost as importantly, I am now capable, because of my addiction, of decency in one respect at least – preferring to buy stuff not for myself but for someone else.

And what a contrast this expedition is, I think, to an incident twenty years ago. Mrs Mouse, with whom I had recently moved in and who was supporting me more or less with the proceeds from a provincial tour of *Doctor at Sea* (in which she played the *ingénue*), particularly wanted me to buy her something special for her birthday. I pulled a face, but she said, 'Don't worry, I'll give you the money to get it with', so I allowed her to drag me round the shops until I suddenly lost my temper and said: 'This is fucking stupid!' Mrs Mouse started to cry, and she continued to cry all the way home on the bus.

I hated that, but I hate it even more when Penny cries. She doesn't often cry, but words frighten her occasionally. If I use words her eyes fill with tears and she looks at me imploringly as if to say, 'Please don't frighten me with words.' And on these occasions I fold her in my arms and I tell her not to be afraid, that words can't harm her.

I can't fold her in my arms, however, when, soon after I get home from the shopping spree, she rings me up and I can tell immediately that she's been crying.

One of the teachers at the horticultural college where she's studying has criticized her homework and since I love her unconditionally – as a parent, I'm told, loves a child – I want to hop straight down to the silly college and bang her teachers' heads together and scream at them and say: 'How dare you make my baby cry!' – just as I still want to seek out and reprimand the wicked Reverend Mother (or whatever the half-witted woman called herself) who in my baby's last report at the convent she attended, said: 'I fear for Penny's future.' What the fuck did she know about my baby's future, the vicious cold-eyed Christian?

'Please don't cry,' I say. 'I hate it when you cry.'

'Sorry,' she says. 'I'll be all right. It's just these beastly axiometrics.'

'What are they?'

'A method of showing garden design in three dimensions. I can't get the hang of it at all.'

'Of course you can. You can do anything.'

And then she asks me if she can come over, but I tell her that I'm working on my memoirs. I'll see her tomorrow, I say.

And since the other thing I can compute instantly in my head is the precise time, down to the last second, until my next fix, I say: 'Only twenty-six hours, eleven minutes and thirty-seven seconds.' And Penny laughs happily and says, 'Only twenty-six hours, eleven minutes and *thirty* seconds now!' – and I think: Dear God I love my baby.

And later I congratulate myself for not having told her about the toys I've bought her. And I reflect too on what a marvellous recipient of presents Penny is. Her eyes light up and she gives great sighs of happiness like a child on Christmas morning. And this is odd, bearing in mind the number of fat money-men with soft white hands and Rolex watches who, after a quick burst of hotel room sex, have given her cash and other tokens of their gratitude.

THURSDAY 7.45 p.m.

It's really good. Your masterpiece. They must be pleased with it, aren't they?

'I think so. I'm quite pleased too.'

It's excellent. You'll be the Jellicoe of the nineties! Next year you could show this at the Chelsea Flower Show.

'It's not *that* good! But I'm getting there.'

And to think that just a few months ago you couldn't do asymet ... asym ... whatever ...

'Axiometrics.'

That's the one. And your teachers made you cry and I wanted to hop down there and crack their heads together. I wanted to say: 'How dare you make my baby cry!'

'That was so sweet. And I still hate axiometrics. But I'm getting better. And Bonita's a help. She's brilliant, Bonita.'

You're better. Another?

'Please!'

Any good?

'Um. Christ! You?'

I'm OK. I'm high just watching you. Can you speak?

'Almost. *Jesus!* What was that?'

What was what?

'I thought I heard someone at the door.'

Probably Pete the Schnoz. He's got extra-sensory perception. He can be on the other side of London and know we're doing this. Customs and Excise are going to replace their sniffer dogs with Pete the Schnoz. He'll be able to sit in Ladbroke Grove and have people busted as they leave Ostend.

'Let him in. He's brilliant, Pete the Schnoz.'

Not likely. We've only got enough for us.

'Oh – right.'

Michael Codron once told me that it was his job, when he worked for Jack Hylton, to check that Hylton didn't attend meetings with lipstick on his fly.

'Goodness. Can I have another? A really big one?'

In a minute. It must be my turn.

'OK.'

Christ.

'What?'

This is good. This is so good. I'm the luckiest man in the world. Who else has everything he wants in front of him?

'I do.'

You do? You *really* do?

'Of course. But what's that got to do with Pete the Schnoz?'

What's what?

'Whoever it was with lipstick on his fly. What's that got to do with Pete the Schnoz?'

Nothing at all. It's for my memoirs.

' Oh.'

They'll all take place in ten hours, my memoirs. It'll all happen during a long conversation between you and me.

'What, a real conversation?'

No. Not *real*. Not exactly what we're saying now. That would be unreadable. All rambling disconnections. And startling profanities. On this stuff, we'd make no sense. There'd be great silences and conversational culs-de-sac. It will have to be controlled. I'll write it up later. But we're the present. Everything else happened months –

or years – ago. I'm telling you stuff. Explaining things. You're listening sweetly. And the past will keep intruding.

'Can I have an . . . ?'

In a minute. I've got to get this bit right. It's important. I think I'll have another.

'Go on then.'

OK. Jesus. Where was I?

'*I* don't know! My turn! My turn now!'

I know. My memoirs. They all take place during this conversation. But there's a snag. Because the general reader might not be interested in September love and regretful personal analysis but only in gaudy revelations about more or less celebrated people, this conversation may make him or her restless.

'Right. Let me have an . . .'

In a moment. This is important. The general reader may think: 'Stuff this. Let's get to the dirty bits. Lady Geldof arse up with Black Claudette. Barclay the Banker roped and squealing like a pig. Pan's People jack-naked in Mrs Mouse's sauna bath.'

To prevent the general reader skipping this ten-hour conversation I'll pepper it with gratuitous asides about well-known people who have never harmed me in the least. To avoid missing one of these the general reader will have to proceed in a systematic manner. Hence the reference to Jack Hylton.

'Brilliant! You're so *clever*! Can I have another now? A really big one?'

OK. Here. You hold the pipe. You look so sweet holding it in your little hands. There's only one thing sweeter. Your walking shoes.

'My *walking* shoes?'

Yes. You turned up one day in shoes you might wear at a point-to-point.

'What's a point-to-point?'

I don't know. Saffy could tell us. She once went out with a jockey.

'That was funny. That night out with Saffy. Let's go out with her again.'

Let's not. She's cuckoo, Saffy.

'I like her.'

You like everyone.

'I don't like *everyone*. I give people a second chance, that's all.'

Anyway, you were wearing these point-to-point shoes and I said, 'What are those?' And you said, 'They're my walking shoes.'

'What's wrong with that?'

Nothing. It broke my heart. You haven't worn them since.

'Well, I wouldn't, would I? Not when I'm . . .'

Working?

'That's *dreadful*! I can't believe you said that! It's *horrible*! Take that back!'

Sorry. Acting?

'*No!*'

Playing?

'Well – OK. But that was *very* bad. I hate it when you say things like that. It means you don't trust me.'

I like not trusting you. That's the point.

'Sorry. I'll get that right. Can I have another?'

Of course. Here. You're still an amazing colour.

'Yes? Shall I show you?'

Later. Show me later. So – it wasn't too bad, Mauritius? He behaved himself, your fat man?

'Christ – I don't want to talk about *him*. What did you do today? Did you work on *Root* with Pete the Schnoz?'

No. He was feeling poorly. I had lunch with Little Jo and then you rang and . . .

'That's *right*. And I caught you listening to that silly Stevie Wonder song. You were thinking about Melanie, I know you were.'

Of course I wasn't. I was working on my memoirs. I've just thought of a great ending. After you dump me, I try . . .

'What do you mean, after I dump you? You may dump me.'

Oh, sure. Anyway – after you dump me, I wait with ever diminishing hope for the telephone to ring. But it doesn't. Not even Pratley rings. So I ring him. And he's out.

'Pratley? I haven't met Pratley, have I? I'm sure you've never mentioned Pratley.'

He doesn't exist. He represents everyone I've been trying to shake off for twenty years. Bitter old men who ring at the wrong time. Who ring when I'm waiting for you to ring. When I'm staring at the phone, willing it to be you. He's fictional.

'Fictional? Is that allowed? I thought memoirs were supposed to be true.'

No. Fiction has to be true. What would count as a lying fiction? In memoirs you can make stuff up.

'Oh. Why am I in inverted commas? You're not in inverted commas?'

It's a literary device. A way of boxing you in. A way of displaying you. You're a trophy. It's a way of controlling you. Only on the page, of course. It's a writer's revenge.

'You've done that before! Is that allowed?'

Absolutely. It's merely a graceful tribute to myself. A retrospective. A summing up. A suggestion that we never learn.

'Melanie was in inverted commas.'

Only until she escaped.

'She didn't escape! You killed her off. That wasn't very nice. You said she was dead.'

She might as well have been. Murdered by Christians in a seaside clinic.

'Well, I hope you're not confusing me with Melanie.'

How could I? You're a million times better.

'Am I? Am I *really?*'

Of course you are.

'Why? Tell me why.'

Later. I'll tell you later.

'Let me have another, then. A really big one.'

OK. Here. Mind you ...

And now, while I wait for the Publisher to return to our table, I brood about my conversation with young Lovering and his insistence – all the more chilling for being delivered on a warm May morning in a Dordogne orchard – that young men and old are locked in an evolutionary struggle for survival.

'Here's an idea,' he'd said. '*Travels with My Uncle*. I *do*. You try to slow me down with intermidable *racontage*. And, of course, we try to kill each other.'

I'd been shocked. '*Kill* each other? You're not serious?'

Lovering had smiled up at me like a venomous angel. Had he been Mr Emmett's nightmare – a manipulative, pouting, silent girl – I'd have been instantly in love. I'd have cranked my vocabulary down, discussed astrology, told him he was pretty enough to be a model. 'Take your clothes off and stand over there by the sink,' I'd have said. Manners maketh man and so forth, but that's how Wykehamists speak to silent women.

'Absolutely,' he'd said. 'The young and the old are locked in a deadly game. To survive, you must usurp my future; I have to kill you because you're in my way. It's the natural order.'

'You *really* want to kill me? You hate me that much?'

'Of course.'

'Why?'

'Because you don't fight fair. The old never do. They rely on their condemned condition to elicit a certain restraint from their vigorous young opponents. Arguing with you is like queue-barging a baglady. I can't humiliate this sordid old codger, I think. And you're an awful reminder of how we must all end up.'

Chilling indeed, and it's as well, I think, that I have decided to tell my memoirs not to young Lovering but to Penny, my beloved.

That said, do the young *really* hate the old so much? Certainly I did, committing many atrocities in my time against the elderly, not least my father.

My father was a very unhappy man whom I remember best drinking gin at 10 a.m. or, on warm August evenings, singing Scottish laments in a darkened room, while my mother played tennis in the softening light with her friends the Pinkneys (Daph and Gee).

'Tonight there are four Marys, tomorrow there'll be but three. There's Mary Beaton and Mary Seaton and Mary Carmichael and me.'

An unusual song to sing in Sunningdale to the sound of mixed foursomes on a suburban lawn.

My father had wanted to be a soft-shoe dancer on the halls or a pianist in the Carrol Gibbons mode, but his father had ruled that he should work in the family shipping-line in Glasgow. Later, my mother ruled that he should live in Sunningdale, which she judged – wrongly, no doubt – to be less common than Glasgow. And so he drank gin disguised as orange juice at 10 a.m. and, while he still could, he commuted between Sunningdale and Glasgow, and this killed him in no time, of course.

I wonder whether I should say this in my memoirs? Shall I say that my mother killed my father by compelling him to live in Sunningdale? It might be significant or seem so.

And here's another telling detail: all his life my father had wanted a boat. He had ships galore, ferrying this and that to Canada from Glasgow, but he particularly wanted a boat. On summer holidays in Broadstairs he'd go into Ramsgate every day to look at the boats for sale. There was one which he particularly wanted, and every day he used to go to look at it.

I asked him why he didn't buy it. It seemed simple enough to me. If you want something you buy it. He smiled sadly. It was too expensive, he said. He shook his head and walked away.

Later, when I was at Cambridge, he threw money at me so that I could kit myself out with a TR2 in British racing green and start literary magazines and be sponged off by Indian poets. We used to drink his gin, the poets and I, and laugh at him behind his back because he didn't understand.

My father's as dead as mutton now and he could have bought a hundred boats. When he died he left a million, enabling me to publish Ted Hughes and Sylvia Plath and, later, to mount satirical entertainments in the West End, to take tea with Peter Cook and wear a silly overcoat.

I brood too about the exact circumstances by which I became a theatrical producer in 1958 – on a whim and after two days as a copy-writer with Ogilvie and Mather (more accurately, the same day twice) – purchasing such goodwill as still accrued to the Jack Waller management, an old-time outfit which had presented *No No Nanette* and other successful entertainments, and purchasing too its 76-year-old general manager, Bert Leywood, who had once been half of a novelty dance duo, Albert and Ivy.

Bert was a sweet old man with Bud Flanagan's beautiful moon face and amused heart-broken eyes, and I treated him with vicious insolence. Irritated by his endless, boring recollections and his habit – affectionately meant, I'm sure – of referring to me as 'the boy', I first tried to blast him out with jokes and cultural references he wouldn't understand and, when this didn't do the trick, I embarked on a campaign of methodical slow torture, moving him into smaller and smaller offices until he and his mementoes of happier days ended up in a broom cupboard in the hall.

Every morning he struggled up from Worthing on the train, thereafter, and uncomplainingly, taking up his position in the cupboard in the hall. And here he'd doze the day away, recalling times perhaps when he hadn't been so lonely, when he and his Ivy had sat together in a Sussex garden and everything had been all right.

One day, when *Beyond the Fringe* was on its try-out tour in

Brighton, he received an urgent message in his cupboard that my boy Charlie, aged two, had knocked a kettle of boiling water over himself and, judging that he should break this to me face to face, he caught the train to Brighton and paddled as fast as his old legs would take him to the Theatre Royal.

Unaware that there was a matinée in progress he stumbled on to the stage crying 'Where's the boy? Where's the boy?' in the middle of some smart skit or other. The audience rocked with laughter and so did I, and this confused him so much that he fell over a piece of scenery and sustained a nosebleed.

'We should keep that in!' said Peter Cook, in an undergraduate comic voice, while Miller and Bennett looked at us with suitable contempt and picked the old boy up. Bennett and Miller's towering moral authority – manifesting itself in ordinary decency to others – wasn't much to the taste, I think, of me and Cook.

So – Lovering got that right. The young really do hate the old. Here's a dilemma, though (and one to be explored as my memoirs progress): when old, is it better to mix exclusively with the young – who will pay you the compliment at least of wishing you dead – or with your contemporaries who, though kinder, will be able to look into your eyes and know subjectively that you've had it? The former, I think, but having it in mind that I might be wrong I resolve henceforth to be nicer to Pratley if I have the chance. Nor is my chance long in coming. I now arrange for Pratley to telephone me bang on cue.

This particular Pratley, who, like all Pratleys, rings at the wrong time, whose telephone manner is at the same time wheedling and defiant, who starts with a joke or a funny voice, sometimes a Goon impression, was a friend of mine in the sixties and, judging that it would be nice for him to see me from time to time, I have, since then, allowed him to buy me dinner once in a while – on these occasions giving him an hour at the most and, to bring it witheringly home to him that I'm in a hurry, insisting that we eat in a pizza bar.

It's the nearest I have ever come to social work, but I always feel better afterwards, rather as my mother must have felt after visiting a former servant now dying in a home.

'How goes the battle in this vale of tears?' says Pratley.

'Try not to be such a cunt,' I say, and I hang up on him.

Pete the Schnoz rings from Bangkok, but before I can tell him the exciting news about the *Root* special he asks me if I'd like him to bring me back some sleeping pills.

I tell him that there's no great urgency in this department; equally, that I'm up for anything these days. Then he tells me a strange story. Pharmacies in Bangkok, it seems, are like English driving ranges, in so far as they have buckets at the entrance in three sizes (tailored, as it were, to the number of balls you want). You choose a bucket and approach the counter, where the assistants are rushing backwards and forwards like McDonalds waiters.

Pete the Schnoz asked for Rohypnol, whereupon the assistant filled his bucket up. Schnoz and Cathy, his beloved, then returned to their hotel, where they made the mistake of having two Rohypnols each, washed down by Bloody Marys.

One Rohypnol, apparently, would knock a police horse bandy, and the next thing Cathy and Pete the Schnoz were conscious of was waking up in the wrong hotel room, handcuffed to the bedpost and with their heads shaved as clean as billiard balls.

'You must have had a good time,' I say.

'Precisely,' says Pete the Schnoz. 'Here's the snag, though: we can't remember a thing about it. Rohypnol seems to erase the memory. We don't intend to make that mistake again. To secure a visual record of tonight's adventures we've just bought ourselves a Polaroid camera. More importantly – are you missing me?'

This is not a casual inquiry, so I answer truthfully. 'It's agony,' I say.

'Did you think I'd found an older man?'

The thought simply hadn't occurred to me, which shows how confident I am in this department if not in many others.

Who, after all could my rival be? Sir Peregrine Worsthorne? Robert Robinson? Keith Waterhouse? It wouldn't have crossed my mind that Pete the Schnoz might choose one of these buffers over me. It wouldn't have alarmed me in the least had I discovered that George Melly was my rival – and Melly, like me, must have black blood in the family, I think, this lucky circumstance allowing him, as it has me, to stay alive longer than is normal, to wear a hat indoors and still be welcome where the music is.

I'd see off Melly in a trice, I think, if he tried to take my Schnoz away from me. So what does it mean, this confidence with men? Rejection by a man – if I've put myself out – is unimaginable. It must go back a long way, this confidence with men, must be to do, I think, with being told that I was perfect by my mother, and I'll examine it briefly in my memoirs.

'Not really,' I say to Pete the Schnoz. 'But it's nice to be kept on one's toes, to be made to feel a little insecure.'

I am missing him, in fact. Like Simon Carr, Pete the Schnoz is unable to be boring, though, like Simey, he often bores himself. Though, like Simey, fitfully gregarious and, like Simey, annoyingly gifted in the area of supper-party expertise, Pete the Schnoz, even more than Simey, tends to slump shortly before 3 p.m., is suddenly nauseated by the fact that he must choose between enduring an ordinary afternoon and frightening the life out of himself with chemically induced euphoria. And so, rather than reality (attending a friend's wedding in a tent, trying to summon up the energy to talk to a madwoman at a buffet lunch), Pete the Schnoz will horrify himself at the nearest place of danger.

That said, Pete the Schnoz, being ambitious, wishing, basically, to find life manageable, can with a straight face sometimes take a meeting down the line with a not obviously all-there film executive on the coast – on top of which he has a steely, manipulative, rather unattractive feminine side which may save him in the end.

Or will it? There have been times when I've seen my Schnoz utterly reduced, slumped on the floor, eyes wide with terror, screaming silently for help. I've been quite alarmed – compelled momentarily to imagine him broken in a seaside clinic, without dignity or self-respect, holding hands in a group and putting his trust in Him up there. Happily, this vision quickly passes. They won't take my Schnoz away from me, like they took Melanie away, put him on a programme for life and tell him, as they told Melanie, never to speak to me again. I'll not lose my Schnoz to a grinning seaside counsellor, any more than I'll lose him to a buffer.

Now he asks me what I'm working on, so I tell him that I'm writing my memoirs. Then I describe the technical difficulties to be surmounted: an appropriate tone and, particularly, the problem of embarrassment.

'Embarrassment?' asks Schnoz. 'What embarrassment?'

I explain that a point I shall inevitably have to make is that, throughout my life, sex, whether in company or not, has been the only department in which I have demanded from anyone taking part the very highest standards of seriousness, a concentration on the text, a closeness, a devotion, a *puritanism* – if you wish to put it like that – of which Leavis himself would have approved. I wish to say that for me only sex hasn't been a laughing matter.

'Of course,' says Schnoz. 'So what?'

'Confessions of this sort,' I say, 'can only make one look ridiculous – a point I shall return to when I discuss my friend Kenneth Tynan. Tynan's seriousness about sex was simply embarrassing.'

'Very possibly,' says Pete the Schnoz. He then urges me to be explicit, none the less, with regard to personal disclosures.

'You must dish the dirt.' he says. 'The sixties. The sauna bath. Fat Swedish girls, over here on holiday, saddled up and ridden round the flat. Lady Whatsit pleasured publicly by Count Suckle of the "Q" Club and his friends; Lord Whatsit thereafter losing his reason, sitting in Janie Jones's kitchen with a saucepan on his head. Your trick with Barclay the Banker. Your twenty-year affair with Curt Jurgens . . .'

'*Curt Jurgens*? What are you on about?'

'Who was it then? You told me once. Elaine Stritch? Acker Bilk? Jack Tinker? *I* don't know.'

'Lord Olivier,' I say.

'Good man. The point is, you must name names. Natalie Wood and Fat Antoinette. Lady Geldof and Black Claudette. Mrs Mouse and the two-way mirror. Carly Simon. Sarah Miles. Simply go for it. Let it all out. The rage. The pain.'

What rage? What pain? Suddenly he's talking about himself, about his own unhappiness.

'What rage?' I say.

'You're a sack of venom,' he says. 'A bladder of self-hatred. You'd prefer to be good – to be living in a nice house with the bills all paid. To be sharing your life with a real woman. To have children's drawings pinned to the door of a family fridge.'

He's still talking about himself, of course – but that's all right. If clothing me in his problems helps him to see them more objectively, that's fine with me. He won't like what he sees. I'll not lose my Schnoz to a thin watchful woman and two unpleasant children. We're bonded by our secret.

'You should let it all out,' he says. 'Say that Albery was a mad old fuck and Dame Lister likewise.'

This disappoints me. He clearly assumes that I have nothing to offer except the transitory and spiteful. Who, these days, would have heard of Sir Albery in any case, still less of Moira Lister?

'That's all in the past,' I say.

'Of course it's in the bloody past. That's what memoirs are.'

That hadn't occurred to me, I must admit. Assuming, later, that the effect of the Rohypnol he's taking in Bangkok will be to wipe all memory of this conversation from his mind, I decide not to rely on him for my supply but to put in my own order for the stuff with Lord Longford's friend, Honest John – thinking, as I do so, that it's worth keeping in with Lord Longford, if only for his criminal connections.

Honest John was resourceful enough, some years ago, to have letterheads printed in the name of 'Honest John – Consultant Neurologist'. He then invited all the leading pharmaceutical companies to supply him with their latest clever drugs. They obliged – the upshot being that Honest John was compelled to rent a warehouse in the Great West Road, such was the volume of smart drugs arriving by every post.

Honest John tells me that my luck's in. He's long in Rohypnol at the moment and can therefore deliver a supply at a sharp price.

So that's good, but now I realize that I didn't tell the Schnoz the exciting news about the *Root* special. It doesn't matter. He'll phone again. The Schnoz's telephonic method is to observe something like the six-tackle rule in Rugby League – always phoning five times before handing you the ball. I know what he really wants, and this knowledge gives me a warm feeling of security. This call – the first of six – means he'll be back in London soon and keen to play.

THURSDAY 8.20 p.m.
'What?'
What what?
'You said "mind you" – as if you were going to tell me something. And then you stopped.'
I did? I said 'mind you'? And then I stopped?
'Absolutely.'
Goodness. Mind you. Mind you. I wonder – I know! I was going to say that it's not that fiction has to be *truer* than biography; rather that it has to be consistent.
'Oh yeah. Right. Of course. Can I have . . . ?'

In fiction things have to cohere. Characters have to be true to themselves. In real life, characters are unknowable to one another. Real life doesn't make sense.

'Right. Just one more and then . . .'

For instance, in my memoirs I'm at pains to set myself up as a certain sort of character. Spoilt. Infantile. Feckless. I say that when I went to Cambridge my father threw money at me so that I could drive a sports car and be sponged off by Indian poets.

'Goodness. Can . . . ?'

But I could just as truthfully have said that I had the iron self-discipline of an elder of the Scottish Kirk. That, like a lot of unusually gifted but over-privileged young men, I worked extremely hard and was rewarded with an excellent degree.

'Wow!'

Exactly. Both versions would be true. In real life a person is an unknowable jumble of contradictory qualities. Brave and cowardly. Cruel and kind. Treacherous and loyal. Feckless and prudent. In fiction this would be confusing.

'I should say so! Can I have . . . ?'

In a minute. This is important. I'm telling you stuff.

'Sorry.'

This is a mistake writers of biography make. They try to shape a life, to give it a fictional coherence. They should just tip the whole mess on to the page and say: 'Here's a life of sorts. Make of it what you will.'

'Is that what you've done?'

What? Where?

'In your memoirs.'

Oh. No. I've made the same mistake as everyone else. I've tried to make sense of it.

'Oh dear.'

A's a bore. B isn't. C's good. D's bad. Ridiculous. How many people are one or the other? Each of us is capable of anything.

'I should say so!'

I've only met three entirely bad people in my entire life.

'I don't think I've met any.'

Well, there you are. Mind you, you've been lucky.

'Yes?'

You've moved in the right circles.

'Of course.'

Users. Tarts. Small-time writers. Dealers. Minor criminals. Bohemians.

'Yeah.'

You've been lucky. You won't meet many out-and-out fucking shits among people like that. Had you mixed more with underwriters, say, or politicians you'd have come across some very wicked people.

'Probably. Here.'

Yes?

'Do you have to be a certain age to be a bohemian or what?'

I think you do, yes. I think you may be on to something. Another?

'Please!'

OK?

'Brilliant!'

Let me look at your eyes.

'Why?'

Melanie used to say, 'Look at my eyes – how are my eyes?' And I used to say, 'Huge. Astonishing.'

'You *are* confusing me with Melanie! I don't *care* what Melanie used to say.'

Sorry.

'So – what was the matter with him?'

Who? What was the matter with who?

'Golly! With Pete the Schnoz. You said you couldn't work on *Root* today. You said he was feeling poorly.'

Oh, right. He was up all night. He was caught in a bust in a crack-house.

'No!'

He was. Quite funny. He couldn't sleep, so he got up, without waking Cathy, and drove to London Airport. Then he drove back. He still couldn't sleep, so he dropped in at Happy's – the crack-house just round the corner from his flat. It's open twenty-four hours a day is Happy's. You just turn up. Excuse me.

'What?'

My turn.

'Have a big one. A real whopper! Go on.'

I think I will.

'Well?'

Christ this is good. This is the best that life can be. Sitting here with the love of my life and a rock the size of Winchester Cathedral. Where was I?

'I don't know!'

Happy's crack-house. That's it. Usual crowd there. Yardies with guns. Lumpy women scarred from knife fights. Will Self and his retinue of *Tatler* girls. Another?

'*Please!*'

Here. OK – my turn.

'Can you *say* that? Is that allowed?'

What?

'About Will Self?'

You bet you can. On *this* you can. On this you can say *anything*. That's the point of it.

'*Yeah!*'

Have a pipe. Sit back. Fuck the lot of them! Fucking cunts, right?

'*Right!*'

No one's safe. I can say *anything*! It's my last chance . . .

'It's *not*.'

It is. That's my justification. I can say what I like. I'm *justified*. It's a question of survival. Take Will Self. Nice young man. Richly gifted. Always been kind to me. Wakes up one day to find that I've placed him in a crack-house in my memoirs. So what? He can take it. He'll survive. But what about me? I think I'll have another.

'That's right. Go on.'

Christ this is good. It never gets better than this. Where was I?

'Will Self?'

Right. Will Self. Here goes. I had dinner with him and Katie when you were in Mauritius.

'You did?'

Absolutely. Just the three of us. After dinner, Will rolled joints. I smoked one, feeling damn foolish.

'*Why?*'

I looked like Denis Thatcher. Old boy, John Lewis Partnership blazer, languidly relaxing. I turned the wrist, said: 'Hey hey hey' – not too loudly. Then it got worse. Will wanted to chase the dragon. Suddenly this nice house in Kensington was full of young people – all girls. Anna Chancellor, Katie's sister, whom I'd last met when she was fourteen. She was best friends at school with Bron Waugh's niece, Claudia Fitzherbert. Claudia and I used to correspond. 'Dear Wicked Uncle Willie . . .' Her letters were remarkable. I'll show you one.

'Where are you going?'

To the literary room. Her letters are in the literary room.

'Careful!'

You're right.

'What?'

Can't seem to make it. Legs have gone. Never mind. You'll have to take my word for it about the letters.

'OK.'

Anyway, she wouldn't meet me. She sent Anna Chancellor instead. I took Anna, aged fourteen, to dinner at the Hungry Horse. She wore her Uncle Alexander's long blue overcoat, I do remember that. She's a successful actress now.

'Who? Claudia Fitzthingy?'

No. Claudia writes – excellently – for the *Telegraph*. Anna's the actress. She was Duckface in that thing.

'What thing?'

That film thing. *You* know.

'Can I have another?'

In a minute. Anyway, I'm sitting there thinking, crumbs, whatever next? Then a theatrical set designer arrived and a plump girl in a top hat who had to do with Condé Nast, I think. Will got the gear and did stuff with silver foil and . . .

'I've got it! This is for your memoirs! One of those indiscreet bits.'

Right. I might use it now, or I might work it in later. I might pop it into a conversation with my sister, Bobo, or when lunching with Little Jo. I might want to confound a nice person with this startling discovery of mine: that it isn't just whey-faced street derelicts who chase the dragon after dinner. So there'll be a serious purpose to this betrayal – or so it will seem. I wanted to leave, of course.

'Why?'

That's what they said. 'Why do you want to leave?' they said. 'I feel out of place,' I said. They didn't want me to go. They said it would be judgemental if I went. Extraordinary. Rather than be judged, these successful young people preferred to get high with an old man in a John Lewis Partnership blazer.

'I understand. I think I'd have felt the same. What about Pete the Schnoz?'

He wasn't there.

'Not *then*. In your anecdote.'

What anecdote?

'Golly. Something to do with Pete the Schnoz caught in a bust at a crack-house.'

That's right. Happy's in Ladbroke Grove. It's so public it might as well be advertised in *What's On*. The mystery is why the police have never raided it. Well, the mystery was solved last night. Pete the Schnoz is sitting there, pipe in hand, high as a kite, discussing the meaning of life with Mrs Happy, when they come through the window. Old Bill, alsations, night-sticks, hosepipes – the works. They hosed down anything that moved. First tubbing Mrs Happy had had in months. Are you following this?

'*Yes.*'

You're not.

'I *am*. Can I have another?'

OK. Here. I'll hold it. So – Pete the Schnoz, thinking rather quickly, says he's me. What do you make of that?

'He did? Wow. When?'

Christ. *Last night.* Right – that's it. You can't have another for at least ten minutes.

'OK. Sorry. I'll be good now. I'll be really good.'

So the police say, 'Who are...'

'Let me have *one* more. Then I'll be good. I'll be really good. I won't ask for another. Just *one* more. *Please.*'

All right. Just one. Here. Better?

'...'

Penny? *Pen?* PENNY!

'Christ! What?'

Are you all right?

'Ummmmm...! Can I have an...?'

No!

'Sorry. Right. I'll be good now.'

So the police say, 'Who are you?' and Pete the Schnoz says, 'Henry Root. *Root Into Europe.* George Cole.' And guess what? The Old Bill in charge turns out to be George Cole's greatest fan. He gives me a bit of a bollocking, of course, and...

'Why? What have you done?'

Not *me*. Pete the Schnoz *pretending* to be me.

'Oh yes. Sorry.'

Then he insists on escorting me home. He personally delivers me to Cathy. 'Good morning, Mrs Root. Sorry to disturb you, but we found Mr Root in a crack-house.' Bit of a shock for Cathy. Thought she was snuggled up to Pete the Schnoz, gets woken at 5 a.m. to find twenty Old Bill in her bedroom with the news that they'd found her beloved in a crack-house. Small wonder Pete the Schnoz couldn't work today. Bit of explaining to do. OK. You can have another now.

'It will be my last. Honestly! I promise!'

Oh sure.

'How are my eyes? Huge? Astonishing? Is that what Melanie used to say?'

Always.

'Poor Melanie. Poor Princess. Tell me again. Tell me why I'm better than her.'

Later. After you've had another. Here. I'll hold it.

'What's happened to the coffee-table?'

It's broken.

'Oh. No, I mean . . .'

I'm glad I haven't made the mistake so far of fishing the Polaroids out of my pocket and showing them to the Publisher – a *faux pas* I now commit in my memoirs while having my hair cut by Miss Vicky of Pierre *et cie*. Miss Vicky also does June Upstairs's head and is therefore a source of gossip.

'June Upstairs been in?' I say.

June Upstairs has set up shop in Camberley where, surprisingly, her business thrives. When I asked her to account for this she said I was forgetting the M4. London-bound personnel with mobile phones, hell-bent on attending software conferences at Wembley, stop off in Camberley, it seems, and visit June Upstairs.

'She was in here yesterday,' Miss Vicky says. 'She's going bankrupt is June Upstairs. She's being chased by Mrs Lamb of the

Inland Revenue for tax on a million pounds.'

'A million pounds! She's doing well.'

'My words precisely,' Miss Vicky says. '"You're doing well, June Upstairs," I said, "considering you're fat and past it." "It's the parking problem, Miss Vicky," she said. "A gentleman on the M4 fancies seeing a London girl and then he remembers the parking problem. I'll see June Upstairs in Camberley, he thinks. There's a lot of gentlemen on the M4, you know, on their way to conferences and that. Plus, they have little conference stickers attached to their lapels: John Punter. Silly Sods Ltd. Bristol. Handy, that, in case they do a runner with the surgical stirrups."'

'Makes sense,' I say. 'Not too much off the back.'

'And she's not taking nothing from Mrs Lamb of the Inland Revenue,' Miss Vicky says. '"I want a down-payment of £97,000," said Mrs Lamb. "Fuck off, Mrs Lamb," said June Upstairs. And now she's working flat out. She had her mobile phone with her and she made six appointments for that very evening.'

'She took calls from her punters here?'

'Sat in the very chair you're sat in now. "It's £100 straight," she said; "£150 for domination." My other ladies was well impressed. "You're working too hard, June Upstairs," I said. "Not really, Miss Vicky," she said. "They're all on my way home." "There's a lot of people on their way home, June Upstairs," I said, "but they're not all stopping off to give domination at £150 a time." My other ladies quite agreed. "You should go off-shore, Miss Upstairs," one of my other ladies said. "You don't want Mrs Lamb of the Inland Revenue catching up with you."'

Nor do I want her catching up with me. Mrs Lamb recently assessed me too – though on a turnover less impressive than June Upstairs's. And going off-shore isn't an option at the moment. Then Miss Vicky asks me what I'm writing.

'My memoirs,' I say. 'Thinking about them, at least. I'm at the planning stage. Construction, tone, attitude and so forth.'

'Attitude? What attitude?'

'My attitude to the material. I don't want to come across as grudging and superior, wheeling on Pratley, say, merely to sneer at him.'

'Pratley?' Miss Vicky says. 'He's one of my gentlemen, I think.'

'I doubt it,' I say. 'He's fictional – a device, merely, and quite a cunning one, even though I say so myself. He represents everyone I've been trying to shake off for twenty years: embittered men of my own age who are calamitously off the pace. I won't – when I come to do my memoirs – wheel Pratley on simply to call him a cunt. That would be entirely wrong, do you see? Quite the wrong attitude.'

'What are they called, then, these memoirs of yours?'

'*From Winchester to This*. The past and the present side by side.'

Miss Vicky's impressed, I think. 'It will be a hot potato, that,' she says. 'You was ostracized, wasn't you?'

I'm shocked. 'Me? Ostracized? I was never ostracized.'

'Yes you was. You was ostracized. By the family. You was a black sheep, you.'

Far from it, as it happens. As I shall reveal when I come to do my memoirs, my parents were devoted to me, particularly my mother. My mother always put my interests first, not least before the country's.

When I was four, and since she could see no reason why wartime restrictions on the use of private cars should prevent me from enjoying Terence Rattigan's latest sophisticated comedy in London, she buried enough black-market drums of petrol in the garden to fuel the Allies' Normandy offensive.

And when I was called up by the Navy she rang up the First Sea Lord and told him that since I had just begun to do the season – waltzing at Claridge's with Lady Serena Lumley, the Lord Great Chamberlain's daughter, doing the two-step with Rutland's future wife, although affianced myself at the time to Isabelle Giscard d'Estaing, the future President of France's sister – he couldn't have me yet. The First Sea Lord realized that he'd met his match and suggested that I pitch up when it suited.

Nor was my father any less resourceful, at least with cash and share certificates. One day, when I was about six, Muspratt the butler appeared in my wing of our house with a message from my father inviting me, if I had a moment, to drop in on him in his quarters.

'William, isn't it?' he said. 'I'm your father. Here's a cheque for £150,000, some share certificates and the title deeds to a shipping-line or two.'

No, Miss Vicky had got that wrong. I was never ostracized. A trifle indulged if anything.

Then she asks me how my Princess is.

'My Princess? Do you mean my baby? Melanie was my Princess.'

'That's right. The one you put in a clinic. How's your baby? Penny, is it?'

'Perfect.'

'That's nice. How long you been seeing her now?'

Apart from my addict's ability to compute my income in terms of presents for my baby, I can also instantly calculate – down to the last second – how long it is since I first set eyes on her and, accordingly, I was able to say to Miss Vicky: 'Five years, three months, seventeen weeks, four days, six hours, forty-three minutes and eleven seconds.'

'Golly,' Miss Vicky says. 'It's beginning to look serious.'

'It is.'

Then, judging that she'd like to see the Polaroids, I fish them from my wallet and pass them over.

'The Polaroids,' I say.

'Oooh I say! Who's this other girl, then?'

'That's Big Tracey. She's my baby's friend.'

'She's very pretty, your baby, but she looks sort of . . . I don't know . . . sort of . . .'

'Respectable?'

'*That's* it! Respectable. I wasn't expecting that. I mean she looks ever so neat and clean. She might be something nice, like a stylist. She looks sort of . . .'

'Ordinary? As if she might work in Kall-Kwik? A crisp girl who you encounter from time to time in Kall-Kwik and after six months you realize that you want to fuck her?'

'Mind my other ladies.'

'Sorry. But you know what they say: no man's truly been in love until he's been in love with a girl who looks as if she works in Kall-Kwik. That's the point of my baby. She's ordinary.'

'This isn't ordinary – what's happening here with Big Tracey.'

'That's my baby's dark side. It's what makes her interesting.'

'I don't want to know about dark sides,' Miss Vicky says. 'I know you went to public school and that, but I've got enough worries of my own without dark sides, thank you very much.'

Miss Vicky is currently seeing a young man in vegetables and I judge that it would be polite now to inquire about *her* personal arrangements.

'Problems with your young man in vegetables?'

Miss Vicky pulls a face. 'He took me to Bournemouth, didn't he?'

'Nothing wrong with that.'

'That's what I thought. But he got unnecessary in the morning. He started to rummage around down there. "Here!" I said. "What do you think you're doing?" "Foreplay," he said. "Well, cut it out," I said. I ask you! Foreplay in the morning. *Men.*'

She gives me back the Polaroids and while she continues to do my head I suddenly remember a remark by Sir Victor Pritchett. Asked what was the most important lesson he'd learnt in a long life, he said: 'Just this – sooner or later everyone wants to be respectable.'

I hope he was wrong – more accurately, that this rule can be reversed. My baby's respectable already – at least in a parallel existence away from me – and my hope is that one day she'll want to be disreputable.

I blame Nan and Grandad, who aren't her grandparents in the

least, I've recently discovered, but the grandparents of her school friend Simon. At the age of eleven, and wanting to be accepted by Simon and his Balham gang, my baby bought herself a pair of football boots, thinking that Simon and his team wouldn't let her play with them unless she had a proper pair of boots. And this, when I think about it, makes me want to cry. And then, at the age of thirteen, and exhausted by her parents' endless drunken brawling, my baby left home in the middle of the night, walked down the road with her most cherished possessions in a suitcase (a teddy bear, some seaside shells collected on a summer holiday in Devon) and moved in with Simon's parents – Neil and Margaret – and with his grandparents Nan and Grandad.

And Nan and Grandad brought her up to be very good at doing things – remembering people's birthdays, wrapping parcels, sewing, cooking, playing tennis (my baby's second serve is forever being reconstructed at the Mark Cox Tennis School) – and now she's at a horticultural college learning how to design gardens with a barbecue area for south London newlyweds. And she has a large dog called Boris and she gives dinner parties and the thought of her wanting to make a go of these almost breaks my heart.

And, to cap it all, she has a younger sister called Susan, who, not having been brought up by Nan and Grandad but by her drunken, brawling parents, isn't respectable in the least but works in a wine bar and sleeps with British Airways personnel. And since her drunken parents can't cope with her behaviour they sometimes bring my baby in to read the riot act. And once, with a straight face, my baby offered Susan £1,000 if she could go six weeks without sleeping with British Airways personnel .

'That was risky,' I'd said. 'Did you lose?'

'What!' Penny had said. 'It was the safest bet I ever made. She slipped up after just three days. Honestly, if I'd slept with as many men as Susan has I couldn't face myself.'

And she'd been unaware of any irony involved. No, my baby's

respectable through and through – which, thank goodness, doesn't mean she ever says anything respectable enough to put me off her. She doesn't say 'Oh ye of little faith!' or, like an arch English actress participating in a comedy-drama by John Mortimer, does she suddenly raise a glass and say: 'To the victor the spoils!' or 'Flattery will get you everywhere, Sebastian!' (She did once, after I'd bought her a dress from Joseph, do a twirl and say '*Voilà!*', but that was a temporary lapse, I think.)

She'll be all right, my baby. She's respectable from the tip of her head down to her smart pair of walking shoes and this will save her in the long run. She's the girl next door, longing for the nourishment of the most ordinary life and ultimately she'll hate me for its withdrawal. (I'm rather pleased with that. Canetti, is it? When I get home I'll have to look up the whole passage in *The Human Province*. Something to do, I think, with its being a writer's drive to deceive the people he loves – deceive them of what they could get from everyone else. It could come in handy when I start my memoirs.)

And thinking about my memoirs causes me to ask Miss Vicky whether she'd be up to running into Our Price and asking for a copy of Stevie Wonder's 'I Just Called to Say I Love You'.

Miss Vicky almost drops her scissors. '*Please!*' she says. 'Not in front of my other ladies. Why ever would you want that? I thought you was groovy, you.'

I explain that the song has nostalgic associations, carries with it a painful undertow of remembered happiness, of Melanie and her trips to Ibiza in 1985.

'It's for my memoirs. When I come to write them I may mention Melanie in passing and, like someone probing a tooth to discover whether a nerve is still alive, I'll want to hear this song again; to find out whether I experience a small comforting stab of misery – not because I miss her, but because I don't. I'll want to dwell luxuriously for a moment on how everything hurts by being over.

'Once, in Ibiza, while I sat at a beach bar on Salinas listening to this particular song, Melanie, to my embarrassment, asked Tanit the Island God to play dolphins with her in the surf, and when he agreed she laughed and waved at me in triumph.

'And that's how I'll always see her – tanned and happy, her worries forgotten for the moment. Melanie was as groovy as could be.'

'Didn't stop her ending up in a clinic, right?'

Miss Vicky doesn't understand.

'Anyway,' she says, 'I thought you was in love with your baby, you. That's not very nice – thinking about your Princess playing dolphins in the surf. I'll not be party to that. You'll have to get it yourself, that song you want.'

Then she returns to the subject of Pratley.

'This Pratley,' she says. 'You'd better be kinder to him. He might be the only person talking to you soon.'

I feel quite foolish – continue to feel foolish for the rest of the day. Miss Vicky has seen right through me – they can do that, these simple women, they can be quite lethal. I should never have shown her the Polaroids. That had been clumsy. Why had I done that? And when did it start, this carrying of Polaroids, this lack of decorum – as if sex were a hobby, like stamp collecting or horticulture, to be discussed enthusiastically in public?

Here's a conundrum, though: sex just *is* more interesting than anything else – more interesting, obviously, than what you had for lunch – but to say so publicly, to admit to it as a prevailing concern, is to make yourself ridiculous; is likely, indeed, to suggest that you're quite unbalanced.

Ken Tynan made himself ridiculous, even in my eyes. He was a very nice man, I think – certainly he was kind to me – but his fascination with sex struck me as unbecoming, even though I shared it. He used to ask me and my wife to dinner and he'd roll joints optimistically and get the conversation round to sex (to sex as a subject, as an enthusiasm, like the corrida or the ballet or a passion for oriental cats) to the discomfort, I think, of his poised and lovely Kathleen.

One day Kathleen rang me up and said she had been com-missioned to write a film script involving a love scene between two girls. She had no personal experience of this, she said, and would be grateful if I could introduce her to a bisexual woman. She was acting on Tynan's instructions, of course. I could imagine him breathing in the background. I played along, swallowed the story whole, later – and because at that time I'd have assumed, like Tynan, that for such an experiment a woman for a living would be needed – I took June Upstairs to their flat in Thurloe Square.

Tynan was nowhere to be seen but was close at hand, I sensed, treading silently from vantage point to vantage point – the whole performance having been set up so that he could watch and listen. He'd made himself look foolish in my eyes, even though in those days (Melanie had not yet educated me) I'd have done the same. Worse, he'd made his wife look foolish, which would have seemed impossible.

Perhaps Tynan's parents, like mine, took him at an impression-able age to see the *Folies Bergère*. Perhaps, like me, he thereafter, and in private moments, brooded over the souvenir programme and was later thrashed for immorality by Pode. Perhaps, like me, he there-after saw sex as an illicit drug to be most excitingly experienced with a silent performing woman off the premises.

That, surely, was the misfortune visited upon me and Tynan at an early age – and upon others for whom sex, to be exciting, must have an edge of shame. Upon Joe Orton, for example. I've had a thought apropos Joe Orton and one I must include somewhere in my mem-oirs. Had Melanie not educated me – had she not taught me that this edge of uncertainty and shame could be achieved at home – I might have ended up like him. Had Orton been educated by his version of a Melanie he'd have learnt to cruise and cottage on the premises, to install in his own apartment not an hysteric in a wig but a tramp gathered on Hampstead Heath. Each night Orton could have read from work in progress to the tramp, told him stuff (as I told stuff first to Melanie and thereafter to my baby) – after which the tramp could have removed his teeth and performed fellatio, not behind a bush on Hampstead Heath but on the premises. Orton wouldn't have had his skull cracked open and, more importantly, life *at home* would have been as unboring as it can be.

Be that as it may, here I am twenty years later showing Polaroids to my hairdresser in the early afternoon. I'm glad, at least, that I haven't yet shown them to the Publisher. The Publisher is not a man likely, I think, to be impressed by the sudden display of another man's Polaroids over lunch. I can't think of anyone who would be – least of all if no shared intimacy has been established.

Pornography, as Peter Brook explained one evening to me and Tynan over dinner, is not properly to be enjoyed in company. Tynan and I wanted Brook to direct *Oh Calcutta!*, but Brook declined. Then he gave us a short lecture on the theatre. Just as the point of a thriller, he explained, was to frighten an audience and the point of a comedy to make it laugh, so the aim of an erotic entertainment could only be to arouse the audience to a sexual climax. This, he explained, would not be possible in a theatre or, if achieved, would in any case be embarrassing. If Tynan and I cared to open a brothel, he said – a place where the rules had been honestly established – he would be delighted to direct it for us.

Brook's analysis was largely correct, I think. Certainly, a possible accusation that it begged the question (assuming, as it did, that *Oh Calcutta!* would be pornographic) fails against some excellent arguments on the subject mustered by Dr Ian Robinson in his book *The Survival of English*. Their thrust, as far as I remember, is that since we live in a society in which the convention is for modesty in sexual matters, it follows that sexually explicit scenes on stage or screen interrupt the artistic rhythm of the work and impose real voyeurism on the audience. Their response is no longer to the play or film but to the real, or simulated, actions of those taking part. This, as Brook had pointed out, would only be acceptable in a brothel.

The analysis equally explains, I think, why my flashing of the Polaroids in front of Miss Vicky was invasive and indecent, inviting a response which would have been embarrassing had it been achieved. I'm relieved that I haven't as yet shown the Polaroids to the Publisher – which isn't to say that there haven't been some aspects of our conversation that I regret.

I wish I hadn't told him all that stuff about visiting the *Folies Bergère* at the age of thirteen and thereafter seeing women as performers only. I'm not sure if correctly balanced people like the Publisher wish to be privy to such personal disclosures; that they wish to be told that you can be pleased only by women whose expertise is guaranteed by the fact that a reward – in one form or another and at some stage in their careers – has been admiringly transferred. I'm not sure if they want to know this.

At least I haven't yet illustrated the point with personal reminiscence; have stopped short at least of telling the Publisher that Melanie was (until Penny inherited the part) the most accomplished in this regard. I'm glad I haven't told him yet that one night in 1985 Melanie and I were sitting outside the Bar Zoo in Ibiza Town when she suddenly said: 'May I ask you something? Promise not to laugh.'

I did want to laugh. She looked so sweet and serious – and I was a little high, on what I didn't know.

Promise.

'Why do men ask me to take my clothes off? They definitely don't ask other people. I've noticed that. My husband's friends were always asking me to take my clothes off. Once, in New York, my husband and a business associate were discussing something quite important. I was in the kitchen. "Hey, Melanie!" my husband's friend called out. "Come in here and take your clothes off. I want to see you with nothing on." I don't think he should have said that, do you? I don't think it was very nice. Should men speak to me like that?'

She looked so sweet, perched on a bar-stool in the inheritable little Katharine Hamnett skirt – while Stevie Wonder sang 'I Just Called to Say I Love You' – that I wanted urgently to reassure her. And she was right in a way – it wasn't very nice, but it was a compliment too. Men knew that she could handle this gauche request; that she had courage enough for them as well; that her confidence would save their awkwardness.

It's because they think you're a tart.

Why did I say that? I'll never know.

'Hey – that's not very nice! That's definition of character! I'll take you through the courts! And don't laugh – I told you not to laugh. That's attempt of court, laughing.'

Sorry. I meant to say that it's because they trust you. Trust you not to leave them feeling vulnerable and foolish. It's a compliment. Really.

And then I said something about Sartre and identity and social roles, but the exact quotation from Sartre wouldn't come to mind and I rather bungled it. I told Melanie that her 'impression' of a woman was uncannily accurate, the performance perfect.

'You're cuckoo,' she said. 'I told you I'd drive you mad!'

I didn't go mad, of course. I did my best to look after her, until one night – and wanting to play a dangerous new game – I told her that I was bored with her, that I wanted her to go home. She looked confused, smiled with uncertain courage like an overmatched sparring partner just before the lights go out, tried to work out whether this was one of the sophisticated jokes with which we kept each other on our toes.

'You don't mean it, do you?'

It broke my heart to play this game, but once I'd started I couldn't stop.

Of course I do. I'm bored with you.

She collected her things and left abruptly without looking back, and later that night, in her own block of flats, she happened to meet Jamie Blandford, who was free-basing with a group of friends. At about 3 or 4 a.m. she rang me up and I could hear laughter and music in the background. She sounded frightened, but I thought she might be acting.

'Please let me come home,' she said. 'I don't like it here. I shoudn't be here. Please come and get me.'

My chest tightened with excitement, it became difficult to breathe. This was the best game yet. I called her a whore, told her to enjoy herself with her new young friends.

'You don't *understand*,' she said, and she started to cry.

I put the phone down and the next time I saw her she looked as if she'd been living in a drain. I went after Blandford with a bottle, scarcely able to believe an act as wicked as his. Thereafter I rescued her, set her up in another flat and, for once, did the moral thing. I supplied her with free-base cocaine myself, judging that it was best to keep her away from Blandford and his evil friends. Then, since her habit was costing me a fortune, I put her into a seaside clinic run by Christians from which she never emerged.

And now I must track down the quote from Sartre, which will come in handy, I think, when I start my memoirs. I doubt whether I'll mention Melanie in these, but the appropriate passage – something to do with identity being the role we impersonate – might apply quite happily to others.

THURSDAY 9.11 p.m.

'I can see *that*, for goodness' sake!'

What? You can see what?

'The coffee-table. That it's broken. I mean, how did it *happen*?'

Michelle fell on top of it.

'Oh.'

While you were in Mauritius with your fat man.

'Right.'

She's learning ju-jitsu. She's not very good yet.

'I suppose not. Can I have . . . ? Here! Who the hell's Michelle? I've never heard of Michelle. Is she real?'

I don't know. I haven't decided yet.

'What are you *talking* about? I want to know who Michelle is.'

Later. I'll tell you later.

'Can I have another, then? A really big one?'

OK. Here. I'll hold it.

'So – what else did you do when I was in Mauritius?'

I saw Debbie Mason.

'Debbie Mason? Why?'

The Kama Chingford. If she can get *The Kama Chingford* up and running we'll be on easy street, you and me. You wouldn't have to go away with your fat man. You'd like that, wouldn't you? If you didn't have to go away with your fat man? Pen? Penny? *Penny!*

'Christ! What?'

No more trips abroad with your fat man again. You'd like that, wouldn't you?

'Can I have another? Just *one* more? A real whopper, and then I'll be good. I promise!'

You're so *bad*!

'I *have* been bad! I've been *really* bad!'

With Tracey?

'Perhaps! If you let me have another I'll tell you all about it. I'll tell you what she made me do.'

Later. Tell me later.

'Let me have *one* more, then. Just one more.'

OK. Here.

'What else did you do? While I was away.'

I did a radio thing. About Peter Cook. A sort of memorial thing.

'Yeah? What was he like?'

Who? What was who like?

'Christ! Peter Cook. What was he like?'

Very nice. Very funny. I liked him a lot.

'Really? I thought you didn't. Why did you say those spiteful things about him?'

When? What spiteful things?

'In your memoirs. You say he wasn't even slightly funny.'

I didn't mean it. I'm like that in my memoirs when I'm not with you. Likely to say anything simply for effect. A kind of attention-seeking. A kind of journalism. This long conversation is a way of showing that you make me nice.

'You *are* nice. You're the nicest man I've ever met.'

I am with you. I really want to look after you.

'You do look after me. No one's ever looked after me better!'

Cook wanted to meet you. He wanted us to go out together. You and me. And Lindy Benson. He seemed to think I knew her. He used to get rather confused, Cook.

'Lindy Benson? Who the fuck's Lindy Benson? Who *are* all these people?'

Just props. People I can tell stories to. They have no value other than as conduits filtering the past and present.

'I thought you were meant to be telling it to me? Tell *me* a story.'

OK. I'll tell you about Carly Simon. I'll have to mention her at some point. When I was in the music business . . .

'I don't want to hear about Carly Simon! Christ, I know about her already. Tell me something else.'

All right. I'll tell you about Winchester. I used to kick a QC up the arse until he blubbed. He wasn't a QC then, of course. He's a QC now.

'Golly. I didn't know you were gay. Are you gay or something?'

Probably not. And no thanks to Winchester. At Winchester homosexuality was greatly encouraged. We used to bathe in the nude in Gunnars Hole, a disgusting stretch of river cordoned off. It was like bathing in bronchial phlegm. In my day the whole school was in love with Johnnie Slattery. When Slattery appeared at Gunnars Hole the word went round in a flash. Cricket matches were abandoned, the chapel emptied, visiting parents were left wandering up side streets on their own – the whole school descended on Gunnars Hole, masters included. They all pitched up, breathing asthmatically on their rickety bikes – Harry A, 'Sponge' Walker, head of history, 'Oily' Mallett, 'Budge' Firth, the school chaplain, and 'Hearty' Hodges, who, to show he was keen, always dribbled a football up to books. All as mad as hatters. They'd stand at the edge of Gunnars Hole with their reedy shanks and ghostly pubic bushes, squinting at Slattery posing on the diving-board.

'What happened to him?'

Who? 'Hearty' Hodges? He became headmaster of . . .

'No. Slattery.'

Funny you should ask that. I thought he'd become a sheep farmer in New Zealand, but I was looking through the Old Wykehamist Roll the other day and I noticed that he now lives in the village of Up Someone, Hampshire.

'No!'

Really.

'So you weren't gay, then?'

Not particularly. I was more of a bully. I enjoyed parcelling up doe-eyed juniors and dropping them down stairwells in a laundry-skip. I'm probably responsible for more than one self-pitying misfit acquiring a sense of humour as a form of self-defence. It's my belief that if you were a bully at school you're less likely in later life to be a fascist; alternatively, to put on a red nose and pull funny faces for Comic Relief.

'Can I have anoth . . . ?

You'll find, I think, that most of the leader writers on the *Daily Telegraph* were parcelled up at public school and dropped down stairwells in laundry-skips.

'*Please* can I . . . ?'

That was so sweet.

'What was sweet?'

The first time you came out to Ibiza. You were a bit apprehensive when I asked you, so I said, 'Don't worry, I'm a Wykehamist.' And you didn't know what a Wykehamist was, so you looked it up in the dictionary and when you couldn't find it you thought it must mean pervert.

'You can't put *that* in your memoirs! People will think I'm stupid.'

No they won't. They'll think you're sweet.

'Well, I don't like it. You've got to take it out. *Now*. Promise?'

Promise. It's already gone. But it's a mistake. I want to set up tensions. Odd conjunctions. Significant contrasts. That's the *point*. A person like me telling it all to a person like you. From Winchester to this.

'What's wrong with this?'

Nothing much, I suppose. Indeed, it must be what I always wanted. It's quite a contrast, though. It started normally enough. A lake in Sunningdale with moorhens on it. Summer holidays in Broadstairs. Tennis tournaments on Lady Mary Burghley's lawn. Later, dancing with well-born spongy girls to Tommy Kinsman's band. My mother hoped that I might step out eventually with one of Lady Mary's daughters. The Cecil girls. Pronounced to rhyme with whistle. Such details were important to my mother. I don't remember their first names. One of them – Angela, perhaps? – may have attached herself somehow to the Royal Family. She's certainly to be seen at Ascot chatting easily to Her Majesty.

All quite normal, and then it was Winchester and 'Hearty' Hodges, who dribbled a football up to books, and 'Budge' Firth, the school chaplain, who in his sermon to the leavers reminded us that were were an élite, trained to set an example to those without our advantages of birth and education. 'Never forget,' he said, 'that you are Rolls-Royces. Less fortunate folk are merely humble Morris Minors who must take their lead from you.' Those were his actual words. It's a miracle that I've turned out as well as I have.

'Can I have an . . . ?'

And then it was the Navy – strapped to a submarine's bridge in

all weathers, towed aft on a seismic pod during torpedo practice –
followed by Magdalene, the duffers' college, and May Balls on a
summer lawn.

'Just a small one, and then I'll be quiet.'

In those days most things seemed to happen on a summer lawn.
Dances. Tennis tournaments. Garden parties. Optimistic marriages.
Everything happened on a summer lawn. I even got married on a
summer lawn myself. I was stupid and vicious enough to marry a
nice girl who just wanted to be ordinarily happy.

We left a summer lawn to honeymoon in the South of France
where, because public schoolboys didn't in those days associate nice
girls – let alone their brides – with indecency of any sort, I read a
pornographic book beside the pool at La Reserve, Beaulieu, having
first wrapped it in the cover of Kingsley Amis's recently published
Lucky Jim.

Peter Ustinov, sunbathing on a neighbouring deckchair, leant
across and said: '*Lucky Jim*, eh? May I have a look?' Having carefully
read a page or two he handed it back without a word, but he may not
have sampled Amis again, I think – equally, and with mounting disappointment, may have done.

All perfectly normal, and then where was I? Wearing an overcoat
in the West End, mixing with Australians, mounting satires and not
a summer lawn in sight. Had it not been for Henry Sherek . . .

'Henry Sherek? Who's he? I'm sure I've never heard of Henry
Sherek.'

Good heavens! Are you following this?

'Of *course* I am. Can I have another?'

Me first. Christ.

'My turn!'

Good?

'Brilliant! So – who was he?'

Who was who?

'*I* don't know. Golly! Henry something.'

Henry Sherek. An immensely fat impresario of the old school. He was so fat that when he died he had to be craned from the window of his tenth-floor flat to the waiting hearse. Everything I learnt about mounting entertainments I learnt from Henry Sherek. Sherek never put on a show whose set, revolve and all, wouldn't, at the end of an irrelevantly short run, look better in his drawing-room than the three-piece suite in place; for the sake of his wardrobe the juvenile lead had to be as fat as he was, and he saw to it that the *ingénue* had the same measurements as Miss Casparry, his sturdily built general manager.

I learnt it all from Henry Sherek. Once I persuaded John Bird that his satirical revue *Here Is the News* would be most happily accompanied by a fifteen-piece strict-tempo dance band placed on stage. When the show folded after one night in Oxford I cleverly inherited fifteen sky-blue bandsmen's suits and, as a consequence, I did the sixties as Geraldo and his orchestra – the reason, possibly, why, thirty years later, I'm doing them again on my own.

All perfectly normal, do you see? Nothing so far to alarm Pode or Mr Emmett, but then I installed a Mrs Mouse and a sauna bath into a penthouse flat in the King's Road and, later, when time was running out, gave my money to girls like . . .

'Like *me*! That's terrible!'

No. Not *you.* I was going to say to girls like Melanie.

'You *weren't.* You were going to say to girls like me. I know you were. You don't think I'm respectable.'

I *do* think you're respectable. I've said that already. I've put that in. I've said that that's the *point* of you. I've said that your natural condition is *après ski*.

'That sounds awful! You're making fun of me.'

I'm not. It's what makes you interesting. More interesting than Melanie.

'*Honestly?*'

Yes. This is all she was. All she could do. You have choices. Melanie didn't. Least of all in fiction. *Imagined*, she didn't have a chance.

'What about Black Simone?'

Black Simone? What's she got to do with it?

'I thought it was quite funny, that. You and Black Simone stand-ing bail for the King of Spain. Did that really happen?'

I think so. Yes, I'm almost sure it did.

'What about Michelle? Does she have a chance?'

She doesn't exist.

'You said she broke the coffee-table.'

All right. She doesn't exist yet. She doesn't exist *fictionally* yet.

'What do you mean? I don't understand.'

I don't know yet whether I'll need to use her. As a character.

'Oh.'

As something *invented*.

'Right.'

By the time I've finished my memoirs this conversation will be in the past and I might have had better ideas.

'Yes?'

Better ideas than using Michelle.

'Oh.'

I'm a writer. I can do what I like! *Christ* I'm stoned.

'Me too. Nice, right? So – who the fuck is she?'

A gangster's moll. A common-law wife from hell. Short skirt, clever shoes, bullet-holes in the passenger seat of the get-away car. Tommy Roche, her common-law husband, was shot in a lay-by in the course of a cocaine dispute. My friend Frankie Fraser, who is a little censorious, particularly disapproves of her. 'William,' he says, 'she's not the sort of person you should be mixing with.' None of this may happen, of course.

'Well, I certainly hope it doesn't! I don't like the sound of it at all. Can I have another? A really big one?'

Of course. Here. I'll hold it . . .

★

I have, since his death, become increasingly unpleasant in public about Peter Cook. And this is odd, because at the time of *Beyond The Fringe* we got on rather well – a consequence, I suppose, of recognizing in each other (at least by comparison with his colleagues at the time, Jonathan Miller and Alan Bennett) something unalterably second rate, a silly disposition (much commended by the likes of Malcolm Muggeridge and Richard Ingrams) 'not to take life too seriously' – ever the slogan by which the idle and overmatched proclaim themselves.

Accordingly, and in a small studio at Broadcasting House this afternoon, I hear myself telling the producer of a radio tribute that I never found Cook even slightly funny. He *tried* harder to be funny, I say, than anyone I've ever met (with the exception of Spike Milligan, who, by contrast, always succeeds in this endeavour), but that's rather different. Trapped by 'Cooky on form', deploying the full range of funny voices Oxbridge comedians can muster, and held by the drunk's intimidating challenge not to look away, one shortly found one's encouraging smile setting into a rictus grin.

And then, in case my position isn't yet entirely clear, I say how embarrassing it was in later years when Cook occasionally suggested a collaboration of some sort. Cook was the kiss of death towards the end, his name on a proposal enough to land it in the bin.

We went through all this on *Root Into Europe*, I explain. Keen to get the thing set up whatever, I would suggest Cook as a possible Root from time to time, whereupon there'd be long faces round the boardroom table at Tiger Aspect Television. Mark Chapman would turn as white as herring-roe and the producer, Justin Judd, would clutch the budget to his chest as if the mere mention of Cook's name would be enough to unravel his clever calculations, and there'd be dark mutterings about drink and drugs and general unreliability.

By the evening I rather regret the ungenerous tone of my thoughts so far (which I had intended to repeat in my memoirs) and, having wiped them from my mind, I decide instead that I'll put in some graceful stuff about the old days. For instance, how Cook was the only one to help me out when Bob Dylan took to sitting in my office in the afternoon and, in spite of all requests, refusing to take his work elsewhere.

In 1961 I maintained a presence in the music business, as everyone did in those days – even having a tie-up of some sort with an American agent whose name I forget. One day I returned to the office after lunch to find a small man sitting on my sofa, strumming a guitar and with his hat on back to front.

'Fuck off,' I said.

It was no good. Every day when I returned to the office after lunch there he was sitting on my sofa with his hat on back to front. In the end, and in self-defence, I tried to get him work but to no avail. My old friend George Martin at EMI courteously listened to a tape but expressed no interest, and Dick Rowe at Decca and Tony Hatch at Pye were equally unimpressed. Only Peter Cook came to my rescue. He put Dylan on at the Establishment – unpaid but with a meal thrown in. Dylan made no great impact and shortly returned to America where things went better for him.

Anyway, that's what I'll do when the time comes. I'll say in my memoirs that Cook's downfall, though sad, was only to be expected. Its cause, I'll say, had little to do with lack of character (which is the received idea) but rather with a lack of talent: a perfectly predictable inability to develop what was in any case merely the quickness of a perpetual undergraduate. To audiences familiar with the real brilliance (both at the creative stage and in performance) of Steve Coogan, say, or Paul Whitehouse or even Harry Enfield, the mystery would be not why the career faltered but how it had ever started. I'll say that the embarrassing gaucheness in performance, the lack of professional technique, was always built in and that once the originality had exhausted itself there was nowhere for Cook to go – except into long nights of self-hatred and excess. And, unlike former colleagues who shunned him at the end, I'll say how grateful I was to

Cook for his unfaltering kindness, both in the old days and more recently.

And later, while absent-mindedly leafing through a stack of mail, I inadvertently open a letter from June Upstairs's friend, Mrs Lamb of the Inland Revenue. Mrs Lamb is assessing me on an income of £87,379.

This is a shock, but then I think, no, hang on, I didn't earn anything like that amount last year, Mrs Lamb has made a mistake. So that's all right. And then I notice that she is referring, in fact, to 1989; that she assumes, indeed, that my earnings then picked up quite sharply; further, that unless I settle the matter within three weeks she will be applying for something called a Statutory Demand. That sounds nasty, but then I notice that her letter was sent three months ago. So that's all right. Since the whole thing is now out of my control it can safely be ignored.

My old friend Black Simone rings. She has discovered that King Juan Carlos of Spain is an impostor, that the rightful King is as black as your hat and is being held in the basement at Windsor Castle, along with the White Russians.

Our man, apparently, is HRH Prince Don Juan Alfonso, the eldest son of King Alfonso XIII and Queen Eugenie Victoria. When he turned out to be black, she says, court officials instructed the midwife to dispose of him. Instead, she smuggled him to Nicaragua. Later, he turned up at Windsor Castle, where, guarded by SAS men, he is being held at Her Majesty's pleasure.

'And we all know what Her Majesty's pleasure is,' says Black Simone. 'They keep you breathing. We should give the man a lifestyle.'

Black Simone's information is sometimes good, but this is pretty weird stuff. I ask her whether she's *sure* this chap is who he says he is – and this is a mistake since she now begins to screech at me, pointing out that his bona fides have been checked out by Eleanor Gall no less. Mrs Gall can confirm that our man wears little slippers with the Spanish royal crest on them.

'What are you saying?' screams Black Simone. 'You saying Sandy Gall is the sort of man whose wife would swallow any old black man's story? On top of which, he has a life-long bus pass. I ask you. What's a black man doing with a life-long bus pass unless he's the King of Spain?'

This is beginning to make more sense, so I ask her what the plan is.

'We'll snatch him from Windsor Castle,' says Black Simone, and take him to a safe house where he'll be debriefed by someone who knows a bona fide king when they see one.'

'My best friend, Little Jo,' I say. 'She'd be ideal.'

And so she would. Apart from being perfect in most respects, Little Jo works for *Tatler* and attends receptions with a matching boy from Hambro's. You'd have to get up very early in the morning to get a bogus king past Little Jo.

'OK,' says Black Simone. 'Then, if he stacks up, we'll fly him to Spain, where we'll confront the impostor, Don Carlos. "Bad news, my man. You're not the only king runnin' around, you know." '

'When do we make our move?'

'Once I get my head together,' says Black Simone.

'Of course. How long will that take?'

'A few days at the most. Then I'll be in touch.'

I'm in two minds. On the one hand, this could be the fictional escapade in the present, which my memoirs so far lack; on the other, the story is a little far-fetched and Black Simone did have a long affair with Reginald Bosanquet, which shows some lack of judgement. Against that, she is quite well connected (she has a flat in Dolphin Square where she often straddles Lord Rippon and whips his quarters while he speaks to the Queen's Private Secretary on the telephone), and a willingness to believe her in the past has often given me the drop on mere tabloid journalists who, obliged to choose between the word of a Tory MP and that of a common prostitute, have been far too stupid to see that you can put your mortgage on the latter being true.

For instance, when Black Simone ran around claiming that her twenty-year affair with the old stalking-horse Sir Anthony Meyer had been real love rather than a casual fling (and waved cheques, billets-doux and her Certificate of Excellence from the Dominatrix's Academy in Amsterdam – fees paid by Sir Anthony – as evidence) no one believed her except me – the upshot being that I met incredulity from one end of Fleet Street to the other, until I managed at last, and after quite a struggle, to sell her story to the *Sunday Mirror* (and to the *People* too – not that I would necessarily want either party to discover this).

Nor, in my memoirs, must I forget to point out that tabloid journalists would prefer (which is an even bigger mistake) to give the benefit of the doubt to the Commissioner of the Metropolitan Police than to the general manager of a brothel.

When my first book, *Both the Ladies and the Gentlemen*, was published, and since I judged that the best way to drum up publicity would be to say that it was all true rather than a fiction, I attempted to grass myself up to the *News of the World*. I passed on various stories to a drunk on that paper, confidant that they included at least one hot potato: the occasion when Sir Robert Mark's daughter, Christina, came to dinner with me and Emma Jane (my employer in the brothel) and Emma Jane did a trick between the soup and fish. Further, and to pepper it up a bit, I told him that Sir Robert Mark's son-in-law, my friend Tim Williamson, far from being an artistes' agent (representing Peter Bowles and others), made ends meet by dealing, quite successfully, in drugs.

I knew this for a fact, I said, because I'd set Timmy up. In 1966 or so Dread the Head, who was Mrs Mouse's dealer at the time, decided to move to Morocco to think things over. For as little as £200, he said, Mrs Mouse and I could buy the goodwill which had accrued to his business down the years – including his main source of supply and his list of clients.

Mrs Mouse and I bought the concession, but when we rang Dread the Head's former clients (pop stars, a drama critic, a professor at the London School of Economics, Princess Margaret's friends) and introduced ourselves as their new supplier they all got the horrors and dropped the phone.

We've been sold a pup here, we thought, so we offered it to my friend Tim Williamson. Tim realized immediately that being a drug dealer was as good a cover as any for someone who ran an artistes' agency and had recently married the Police Commissioner's daughter.

He was bored, in any case, with Peter Bowles arriving in his office and wanting to know why he hadn't been put forward as the new James Bond.

Tim and Christina's social life improved quite noticeably – as it tends to if you're supplying Princess Margaret's friends – though whether Christina fully understood the reason for this circumstance I never knew for sure. However, and as I pointed out to the drunk at the *News of the World*, all would become clear to her if he cared to reveal the matter in his paper.

Not a chance. He presented some sort of story to his editor, but the latter ruled that it must be untrue. It was not conceivable, he said, that (a) the Commissioner of the Metropolitan Police's daughter would have dinner in a brothel and (b) that the Police Commissioner's son-in-law would supply drugs to Princess Margaret's friends.

This will be one for the memoirs, I think – though whether I shall reveal that Timmy came unstuck in 1977 and killed himself is something I shall have to consider more carefully as I proceed. And that was an odd business. So far only two of my close friends have come unstuck, as far as I know (the other is Simon Dally, who published *The Henry Root Letters*), and the symptoms displayed by both were so comically exaggerated that we all supposed they must be feigning madness – though whether to wrongfoot their creditors or to get on television or to become a success in public life we couldn't guess.

Dally's case was as peculiar as Timmy's, and he didn't have the excuse that he represented Peter Bowles. Shortly after the *Root Letters* were published Dally initiated a coup against Lord Weidenfeld, first bugging his office (for what purpose was never clear) and then inviting Ray Compton, Weidenfeld's managing director, to join him in the insurrection.

Compton informed Lord Weidenfeld and Dally was given half an hour to clear his desk. Undeterred, Dally then evolved a plan to control the world from a computer database in W11, the first stage in this scheme being to bug his own flat in Leinster Terrace and let it to a call-girl ('Knowledge is power,' as he explained to me one night). Nothing much came of this, so he palled up with Lord Keynes next door and one night, when Keynes was away in the country, Dally let himself into his house and stole his library – later trying to sell it off at Christie's. The police were informed and Dally shot himself. Odd, really. A publisher, of all people, should have known that books are almost impossible to sell.

Be that as it may, I now ask Black Simone whether she is man enough to walk into a branch of Our Price in search of Stevie Wonder's excellent hit single of 1985, 'I Just Called to Say I Love You'.

'It has nostalgic associations,' I explain, 'to do with Melanie and Ibiza and . . .'

Black Simone cackles disbelievingly and turns me down. This surprises me, since I had assumed that blacks have too much social confidence to fret over the opinion of a multi-pierced youth in a record shop. I say as much to Black Simone, whereupon she accuses me of making racist assumptions and then hangs up on me.

This accusation is wide of the mark, as it happens. In fact, I'm black myself on my mother's side of the family – according, at least, to my Aunt Bessie (on my father's side), who used to make this claim to irritate my mother. My mother was a Christian on her mother's side (she was a direct descendent of Mr Fletcher Christian of the Bounty), and it was Aunt Bessie's contention – and one I have no reason to doubt – that, having married a local girl on the Pitcairn Islands, Fletcher Christian fathered a number of children. Occasionally, according to Aunt Bessie, someone pops up in the family who's as black as the ace of spades.

Pratley rings back, with an amusing variation on his usual opening line.

'We got cut off,' he says. 'I was going to ask you how you're surviving the slings and arrows of outrageous fortune.'

I decide to get this over with. I don't hang up. I maintain a haughty silence, obliging Pratley to come in at a different angle.

'Still writing, are you?' he asks.

'To my embarrassment,' I say. 'Still churning out best-sellers and smash hit TV shows. I haven't given up, however. I keep my dreams alive, cling to the hope that one day I may fulfil my real ambition.'

'And what might that be?'

'Driving a minicab,' I say.

Pratley's tone becomes a shade less insolent. He's picked up the general level of the irony, I think.

'What are you working on?' he asks.

'My memoirs,' I say. 'Planning them, at least. Construction, tone, attitude and so forth. I don't want to come across as grudging and superior, sneering at old friends who are calamitously out of it. I don't want to sneer at the sort of people who ring you up at the wrong time, who are too stupid to realize that there's only one person you want to hear from.'

'And who's that, may I ask?'

'My dealer.'

'Good heavens! Who's your dealer?'

I must have told him often enough, but one of Pratley's most irritating characteristics is to plant his own thin life centre stage, to talk about himself and his arrangements for all the world as if they mattered as much as mine.

'Penny,' I say.

'And what does she sell you?'

'An imitation woman. A performance. It's entirely inauthentic what we do, quite unreal and therefore imperishable, I think – continuing, like any performance, to live on as a fiction in World 2. Or do I mean World 3?'

I pause, momentarily confounded by my ignorance. As a rule I have enough Popper at my fingertips to get past a *Spectator* essayist or a quacking *Tatler* girl in a Fulham brasserie or, on the telephone, past a resentful friend.

'Never mind,' I say. 'We're trying to cheat death, do you see? If it's a really bad day it's because my dealer has invented an exciting new game. When she's going to withdraw my supply for a couple of days, she says: "Don't worry. I'll be in touch. I'll phone you on Sunday." I cancel everything, switch off the answering-machine and stare at the telephone, defying it not to ring. She doesn't call, but Pratley does. This is Pratley's chance.'

Pratley walks right into it, asking me who Pratley is. I explain that Pratley is everyone I've been trying to shake off for twenty years, and then I describe how, after I've told Pratley to fuck off out of it, I try to distract myself by watching a game of American football.

I'm a Wykehamist, I say, and Wykehamists thrill particularly to the sight and soft satisfying thud of fat men running into each other at 30 m.p.h., but even the exhilarating spectacle of a coked-up linebacker spearing a quarterback headfirst into the ground can't make up for the heavy, dreadful fact that my dealer hasn't rung. I go to bed and toss and turn with a pain like dysentery. 'Someone else feeling her breasts and cunt/Someone else drowned in that lash-wide stare/And me supposed to be ignorant/Or find it funny, or not to care.'

This snatch of half-remembered Larkin will be lost on Pratley, but I press on anyway, telling him that on good days, on days when I'm due for a fix, I'm the happiest man in the world. I feel sorry for anyone who isn't me. I'm so happy I can't sit down. I arrive early for our rendezvous, often a restaurant I'd not be seen dead in as a rule.

When she walks in I almost faint with happiness. Once did. Once, at Bibendum, I passed clean out with happiness. When I recovered consciousness I discovered that she'd availed herself of this opportunity to have an early night.

Normally I blast her with adoration. It must be terrifying, like having the door of a furnace suddenly opened in your face – to borrow an analogy due, I think, to Lady Longford.

'You're perfect,' I say. 'I can't live without you.'

'Thank you ever so much,' she says. 'By the way, I'm off to Mauritius in the morning with my fat man from Cornwall. I'll phone you from there.'

She won't, of course – and this is what makes her the least boring person in the world – but Pratley will. This is Pratley's chance.

'Not a bad life, I think you'll agree. Better than reality. Or perhaps you'd prefer to hear about my attempt to defraud Sir Donald Albery in 1961? J. P. Donleavy's *Fairy Tales of New York* had just opened at the Comedy and . . . Hullo. Hullo. Pratley? Are you still there?'

He's hung up. Never mind. I'll tell that anecdote to Penny, my beloved – of whom I have just given an entirely false account to Pratley. *That* Penny was a fiction, created by me soon after I met her as a precaution against her boring me. It is a role, too, in which she often, and obligingly, excels, delighting me with her youthful, absent-minded candour, her thrilling unconcern. Directed by me ('You're not being pretty enough; you're not being elusive enough;

go off and come on again') she is able to act all the attributes of the ideal other woman: a bruising indifference, a promise in her unfathomable, unconsoling eyes that if you were cold and afraid and needed her she'd be amusingly occupied elsewhere.

And so I brood about her now, about how, when the time comes, I'll describe her in my memoirs, how I'll make sense of her to those who have never had the patience to create the ideal other woman – a careless girl who, even without drugs, can take you into a possible world where it's always after six o'clock and the people who want to get you into trouble have all gone home for the day.

Melanie, whose role Penny inherited, had been the first. An uneducated girl from Harlow New Town, Melanie had taught me that being in love (the drug of my choice, I soon discovered) is a decision; that it can be self-administered at a price; and, most importantly, that fidelity can be made unendurably exciting by endangering it constantly with nursery games.

In 1985 Melanie came out to Ibiza for the first time, and, from the moment I met her in Arrivals, she engendered in me – slung up, as I was, in the traction of my disadvantaged background (Sunningdale, Winchester and Magdalene) and being less socially assured, therefore, than this uneducated girl from Harlow New Town – mixed emotions of embarrassment and pride.

She was looking very pretty, actually, and fairly mad. Her eyes were shining and excited and she seemed to be on the edge of some enormous joke. She kept laughing – not nervous laughter but the deep, serious laughter of someone who's seen a fat woman sit on a chair that isn't there. For Melanie the 'real' world, the world of dry-cleaning and Mrs Lamb, of cling-wrap and special offers, of DIY and Pratley and Statutory Demands, had sat on a chair that wasn't there and was looking very silly indeed.

And later, sitting outside the Bar Zoo in Ibiza Town, I felt light-headed and reckless. She was staring at me, her eyes were enormous and unnaturally bright, and I had a feeling that everything had gone dark around her, that her eyes were glowing brilliantly in a black sky. I hadn't felt like this since Mrs Mouse and I had dined with a Harley Street gynaecologist in the sixties and he'd laced the drinks with mescaline. And she was smiling at me, as if she understood, as if she could see into my brain. This uneducated girl from Harlow New Town could see into my brain.

'This is the best, right?'

I wasn't sure. It was frightening really.

'This is what I do. This is all I do. I give a man everything he wants and then a light goes out.'

What do I want?

'Only what isn't allowed.'

Is this allowed?

'Of course it isn't!'

That's all right, then. What else do I want?

'Could be me.'

That wasn't possible. That had never happened – except in day-dreams about a nicer life. I'd wanted to laugh at her affrontery, but I hadn't laughed. I'd chosen not to hurt her feelings. Manners maketh man and so forth, which isn't such a silly saying after all, I think. You start by being polite, which is pretending to be kind, and it pays so well that it becomes second nature and the artificiality no longer matters.

'Don't look so surprised. It could be me. Not the real me, of course. Just the character you want me to play. You may create a monster! You may have to kill me!'

What's real?

'London. The horrors in the night. People crying on their own.'

Are you playing a part now?

'A bit. I'm figuring you out. I'm getting there. You like silly women. Exhibitionists. Something you discovered when your parents took you to see the *Folies Bergère* in London. You were thirteen and after that you saw women as performers only. Tanned and naked. Prowling a stage. Proud but silent. Safe. Caged. I got all that. You thought I wasn't listening, but I was.'

Caged? I didn't say anything about caged.

'OK – not caged. But prowling. And silent. Perfect. Not *real*. Don't worry. I can do all that. That's easy. I'll find out what you really want and I'll give it to you. But you won't thank me for it. You may go mad!'

That was Melanie, and I didn't go mad, of course. I survived to put her in a Christian clinic from which she never emerged, and writing about her later was a piece of cake.

But Penny's different. Penny's actions connect with one another. She has a past. Things have led to other things. She lives in a proper house and she shops and she avoids the maximum rate of interest on her credit cards. She has a smart pair of walking shoes and she likes on Christmas Eve to attend a candlelit carol service in a local church. Clear-eyed and rosy-cheeked, she always looks as if she's just stepped off a Colorado ski-run.

Why, then, is she systematically mysterious – in every way more mysterious than Melanie? With Melanie, nothing was hidden. She was obviously what she was and nothing else – and she didn't have a chance. But Penny may have something concealed, I think. Under the demure exterior there may be a habit of guile – a potential for deceit inconceivable to me – formidably controlled. Or perhaps there isn't.

Certainly her own attempt to explain the mystery – offered soon after I met her in answer to a chance remark of mine – wasn't helpful in the least.

'There's something odd about you,' I said. 'A quality I've never come across before. It's got me baffled.'

'I'm happy,' she said.

That was part of it, without a doubt – and very unsettling, too (I'd not previously come across someone who *knew* that they were happy), but hardly helpful. What, after all, can you do for a happy person other than to hint that, for the sake of narrative complexity, you intend to spoil it for them? I definitely love her unconditionally, as a parent, I'm told, loves a child – may wish, in a random exercise of imperial parental love, to imperil her in such a way that only I can help – but I want her to be happy always.

THURSDAY 9.48 p.m.

'Christ! What's this?'

What? Where?

'This photograph!'

It's Michelle.

'*Michelle?* You said she didn't exist.'

She doesn't.

'*She's wearing my Katharine Hamnett skirt!*'

She can't be. You're wearing it.

'It's mine! I *know* it is. What's going on? Tell me. Tell me now.'

Don't worry. It's just an idea. For my memoirs. I've thought of another possible ending. When you dump me . . .

'Stop saying when I dump you. You may dump me.'

Of course. Anyway – after you've dumped me I was going to ring up Pratley, but Pratley won't speak to me. Now I've had another idea. I thought it might be better if I'm left telling it all to this sociopath from hell. She'll have inherited the little Katharine Hamnett skirt and the inverted commas. A suggestion that your 'part' can be taught. That it's inheritable. Cute, eh?

'*Fucking* cute! I'll make damn sure you don't meet Michelle!'

Don't worry. I won't – unless you dump me.

'That's all right, then. So – how did she break the coffee-table?'

I told you. She's learning ju-jitsu. She came round here and said, 'Stand absolutely still.' Then she swung herself through 180 degrees and landed on her arse. 'What the hell was that?' I said. 'Ju-jitsu,' she said.

'Are you *sure* this hasn't happened?'

Absolutely. It's all in the mind.

'If you say so. Weren't you alarmed?'

When?

'When sodding Michelle suddenly lunged at you.'

Not in the least. I've found that women have quite an appetite for violence but little natural aptitude. Unless you let a woman get behind you she can be boxed off pretty easily. If she gets behind you you can have quite a fight on your hands. I once let Mrs Mouse get behind me and she flattened me with a salad bowl. Entirely my fault, of course. I'd found her in bed with Fat Antoinette and a crap actor. The actor was dressed as a girl. Naturally Mrs Mouse was very cross.

'Who was he?'

Who was who?

'Crikey! The actor. Who was he?'

Juvenile lead. Thin legs. Odd way of speaking. I told you his name originally, but the lawyer took it out. Afraid of libel. Can't think why. I've only been sued three times – once by Nigel Dempster, once by the Duchess of Argyll and twice by *Private Eye*.

'That's four times.'

I said that Dempster was always thoughtful enough not to wake his sleeping wife when he returned late after finishing a story. Once he undressed in the hall and crept silently up the winding staircase with his clothes tucked under his arm. Then all hell broke loose. He was on the top deck of a number 14 bus. Dempster sued and won. What do you make of that?

'Why was he dressed as a girl?'

Who?

'The actor. The one in bed with Mrs Mouse and Fat Thingy.'

It was the sixties.

'Of course. Can I have another? A really big one?'

Here. What?

'What what?'

You were going to say something.

'No I wasn't.'

You were. You've got something up your sleeve. You were going to tell me something. I know you were.

'Later. I'll tell you later.'

Is it good?

'It's good for me, I think.'

What about me? Is it good for me?

'I hope it's good for both of us. What happened then?'

Nothing. I was knocked cold, wasn't I?

'By *Michelle*?'

No. By Mrs Mouse.

'I know *that*. I mean what happened with Michelle?'

She picked herself up and had another go. 'It doesn't hurt,' she said. 'We've been taught how to fall.' Quite unnecessary in her case.

'Yes? Why's that?'

She was on laughing gas.

'*Laughing* gas?'

That's right. She's discovered that nitrous oxide (laughing gas) is used in industrial whipping machines supplied to ice-cream parlours. If it wasn t for laughing gas knickerbocker glories would be as flat as pancakes. Every evening Michelle hops along to Covent Garden, where she nicks tomorrow's delivery of laughing gas from outside an ice-cream parlour. Then she does stuff with balloons and so forth, and the next thing you know she's on the ceiling.

'She sounds all right, Michelle. I definitely don't want you to meet Michelle.'

I won't unless you dump me. Anyway – Michelle on laughing gas could be bounced off all four walls of a squash court and she wouldn't feel a thing. So, she picked herself up and had another go. 'Stand there,' she said. Up went the little fists, a short sequence of oriental fighting grunts and she flew through 180 degrees, this time landing on the coffee-table, which she smashed to bits.

'Golly. What did you do?'

I laughed like hell. It was the best laugh I've had since *Nights at the Comedy* in 1964.

'*Nights at the Comedy*? What on earth was that?'

My biggest theatrical flop. At one point . . .

'Look – if you've been winding me up about Michelle just so you can slot in an anecdote for your memoirs I'll be *really* cross.'

Sorry.

'I'll need another now. A big one.'

OK. Anyway – in *Nights at the Comedy* we offered anyone in the audience £50 who could knock a 28-stone, black-belt Buddhist monk from Streatham off his feet; £50 was quite a lot of money in those days, but we thought we were pretty safe. A tiny little man in a dinner-jacket climbed on to the stage. We're all right here, we thought. Our £50 is as safe as houses. Hah!

'Let me have another. I need another.'

OK. Here. Don't you want to know what happened?

'What happened when?'

Christ! When this tiny little man challenged this 28-stone judo expert – and us thinking our money was safe?

'Oh sure. Sorry. What happened?'

Nothing at all. The little man couldn't budge the fat Buddhist in the least.

'What! That's a completely pointless story.'

I know. I got it wrong.

'Well, you'd better get it right when you do your memoirs.'

I will. Of course, *Nights at the Comedy* wasn't my biggest flop. My biggest flop was . . .

'This laughing gas. Can we get some? I'd definitely like to try some laughing gas.'

Laughing gas? I don't know anything about laughing gas.

'Oh. In that case, can I have . . . ?'

Don't you want to know what my biggest disaster was?

'Of *course* I do . . .'

I hope that my employers at the *Independent* don't discover that they and Black Simone are about to stand bail for the rightful King of Spain. Black Simone rings to say that our man has been snatched from Windsor Castle and is to appear in court on Tuesday morning.

'On what charge?' I ask.

'Unacceptable behaviour,' says Black Simone.

'Is that an offence?'

Black Simone chuckles briefly at my naïvety. 'It is if They say so.'

'And who are They?'

This is almost too much for Black Simone, who now adopts a tone of pained forbearance, as if addressing the village idiot.

'The people who run this country,' she says. 'I told you they'd get him. I want you to appear in court on Tuesday – either as yourself or, better still, as the *Independent* – so that you can stand bail for His Majesty.'

She then informs me that once bail has been agreed His Majesty will come and live with me. It seems that They have put a padlock on the door of his room at Windsor Castle for unacceptable rent arrears, at the same time confiscating the last of the crown jewels. These consisted, Black Simone tells me, of a tie-pin with a ruby in it and His Majesty's best set of teeth, fashioned out of gold and worn only on state occasions. I gather, in fact, that His Majesty's unacceptable behaviour includes an instruction that all his accounts should be sent directly to the Queen at Buckingham Palace with the request that she should settle them immediately.

Meanwhile, I have agreed, I think, to appear in court on Tuesday as the Editor of the *Independent*.

★

Lunch with my sister Bobo. She is cross with me for proposing to say in my memoirs that, according to old Aunt Bessie, we're as black as your hat on our mother's side of the family. Nor does she care for the picture of our mother that may emerge.

'Aunt Bessie was just an old mischief,' my sister Bobo says. 'She said such things merely to irritate Mother. And Mother was a marvellous woman, as you very well know. You're making her out to be a rather vulgar social climber.'

This is fair comment, but, as I now explain, I can be excused on the grounds of literary strategy. I want to show, when I start my memoirs, that the present affects one's perception of the past – indeed, that it radically alters it – as much as the past determines the present. In fact, I was extremely close to my mother and I treated my father with callow disregard, but it suits my literary purpose now to say that my mother was at fault, that, quite possibly, she destroyed my father's life.

Not only would this version be easier to write and more dramatic (my father, at the grand piano, awash with alcohol and disappointment; my mother, disgusted by his weakness, excluding him from his children's good opinion), it would reflect better on me, I think; would suggest that I feel remorse for the way I treated my father; that in this regard I have grown kinder than my sister Bobo.

And now, to my regret, I produce a smart remark – something I had been determined, before this lunch, at all costs to avoid. I had been determined not to be smart or argumentative, not to present myself – as I usually do with my sister Bobo – like an over-excited undergraduate imparting information that his world-weary parents have assimilated thirty years ago but to show some interest for once in her and her arrangements.

'A valid syllogism,' I hear myself saying, 'conveys the truth in both directions. Its conclusion refutes, or secures, its premises as much as vice versa.'

My sister Bobo is too kind to cut me off at this point, so I continue.

'Consider this: "All animals fly. A pig is an animal. Therefore pigs fly." The argument is coherent, so the conclusion entails the untruth either of the major or the minor premise. Equally, the past is interpreted by present conclusions. My memoirs, when I write them, could as easily be entitled *From This to Winchester*. Biography is invariably partial and mendacious.'

I am quite struck by this idea, which has only just occurred to me – more struck with it, I think, than my sister Bobo is. To my surprise she now tries to change the subject, asking me suddenly whether I have noticed that someone called J. G. W. Davies has died. Having no idea who J. G. W. Davies is or was (some obscure figure from Sunningdale, I imagine, a friend of my parents perhaps), I ignore my sister Bobo's question and continue with my argument.

'Here's my point, however: some of what I write about Mother will be true. During the war, and in order that you and I could be driven to London to see Jack Hulbert and Cicely Courtneidge, she *did* bury enough black-market petrol in the garden to fuel the Allies' invasion of Normandy and, when the Navy called me up, she *did* telephone the First Sea Lord to tell him that I couldn't join until I'd done the season.'

My sister Bobo is confounded for the moment (perhaps she is still worrying about the late J. G. W. Davies – whoever he might have been), so I remind her of the time during the war when Saunders, our chauffeur for twenty years, came up trumps. The Luftwaffe, aiming at London, dropped their bombs on Sunningdale, whereupon Saunders, assuming that the invasion had come at last, seized one of my father's shotguns and placed himself four-square outside the dug-out's door.

'The Germans will get at you and the children over my dead body, ma'am,' he said. Three panzer divisions could have come through the privet hedge and Saunders would have stood there potting at them.

After the war, Saunders voted socialist, whereupon Mother sacked him on the spot.

'That wasn't very nice,' I say to my sister Bobo.

'No,' she admits, 'but you can't really blame her. It's how people like Mother *were* in those days. You could say that she didn't know any better.'

This doesn't strike me as a very good argument, and I would have said as much had my sister Bobo not changed the subject again – not, to my relief, with further mention of J. G. W. Davies but by saying that she is worried, too, about how she may emerge in my memoirs.

'I would prefer on this occasion not to come across as some sort of madwoman in a hat,' she says, 'carrying a stick and barking at labradors in Hampshire.'

In fact I don't think my sister Bobo has been presented in previous stuff of mine as unbecomingly as she always maintains. For instance, Alan Brien, with whom I had lunch the other day, said he imagines her as 'Nancy Mitford on speed'. I now pass this on to Bobo and I dare say she's quite impressed.

I intend, in any case, when I start my memoirs, to present her as she really is for once: not barking or formidable in the least – or formidable only in the sense that she sets an example of simple decency which I can't follow. If I avoid her for any length of time it's because she makes me feel ashamed; because she's the person above all whom I'd prefer not to disappoint.

Which is why I had resolved before this lunch not to be smart or argumentative; not, for instance, to produce from my briefcase the latest evidence suggesting that hard drugs should be legalized. Sometimes in the past I've done this with my sister Bobo, and she hasn't been greatly reassured. Apart from raising four unusually satisfactory – indeed, remarkable – children she has borne the tragedy of a fifth dying as a result of drugs. For some reason, usually lost on me, she has never been much interested in arguments for legalization. Having been determined, on this occasion, not to bring the matter up, I'm quite surprised to find myself producing from my briefcase a clutch of papers by Dr John Marks, consultant psychiatrist to the Mersey Health Authority, and by Professor Ronald Siegel of the University of California.

'This will interest you, Bobo,' I say.

I then tell her that Professor Siegel has recently discovered that, for several years, hundreds of little old ladies with arthritis have been treated in a California hospital with Esterene – a trade name for crack cocaine – without a single case of abuse. It has done nothing for their arthritis, Siegel admits, but it has cheered them up for a while and, having been discharged from hospital, none of them has become an addict. If crack could be taken without abuse, Siegel realized, then the difference between use and abuse was one of context. Calvinistic pharmacology, Siegel argues, has prevented us from seeing pleasurable changes in mind or body as fulfilling health needs. It is time, he thinks, that we recognize intoxicants as treatments for the human condition.

'What do you make of that, Bobo?' I say.

Rather than give her time to answer, or to put me off my stroke by further mention of J. G. W. Davies and his no doubt tragic death, I now bring Dr Marks's latest arguments swiftly to her attention. Dr Marks, I say, has, by the controlled prescribing of heroin and cocaine at two Merseyside clinics, reduced drug-taking and acquisitive crime in the area and brought about a remarkable improvement in addicts' health. His figures, indeed, are even more impressive than those achieved in Amsterdam, where a libertarian attitude to drug-taking has produced a situation which should be the envy of every other European country.

I pause for a moment, allowing my sister Bobo to step in with a black-belt, knock-down argument.

'But who'd want to live in Amsterdam?' she says.

Pondering the matter later I am unable to conclude that Bobo's position is obviously irrational. The legalization argument is utilitarian – at least consequentialist – and nothing could be easier than to manufacture traps for the unwary utilitarian. It is not clear, for instance, that everyone would wish to live in a society which, by compelling its citizens to watch obscene films on television, had, by some process of general catharsis, rid itself of all other forms of sexual abuse.

Equally there seems little doubt that the madwomen who rattle handcuffs at the Conservative Party Conference and squeal excitedly for the return of the rope do so not because they seriously believe that capital punishment is a deterrent but because they *like* it (just as decent people would oppose its reintroduction even if it were shown that its continuing absence was causing the murder rate to soar).

Further, I realize that, were it a question of alcohol being banned, I'd be as deaf to consequentialist arguments as my sister Bobo is when the legalization of other, and perhaps as harmful, intoxicants is being mooted. While recognizing that the prohibition of alcohol would cause a huge increase in human misery, I'd still be more comfortable in a society in which the stuff was banned.

Then, wondering whether my preference for a society free of alcohol and Bobo's for one free of other drugs were aesthetic rather than moral, I decide to check the matter out with my friend Ted Honderich, Grote Professor of Mind and Logic at University College, London.

'I'd be most grateful,' I say, 'if you could put me straight on this. Suppose it were argued – as it has been argued recently, I think, by Roger Scruton – that consequentialism is refuted by the case of a society which, by staging public knife fights to the death, had rid itself of all other forms of violence. Does such . . .'

'Scruton, you say?'

'Indeed.'

'I was not aware,' Professor Honderich says, 'that Scruton has done any serious work in moral philosophy.'

And this, of course, is one of the great joys of talking with distinguished academics: the elegant dismantling of a colleague's reputation.

'The argument,' I explain, 'appears in *The Meaning of Conservatism*.'

'Which is not, of course, a contribution to philosophy. However, what's your point?'

'Do such arguments refute consequentialism?'

'Not my version of consequentialism,' Professor Honderich says. 'My theory expressly demands that the consequences of an action should not issue in an injustice. Clearly, public knife fights to the death do yield an injustice, so consequentialism is not refuted – whatever Professor Scruton might maintain.'

I'm not entirely satisfied, so I give another example.

'What about my sister Bobo's argument that she'd prefer not to live in a society which, by making hard drugs easily available, had rid itself of the drug problem. Might she not escape on the grounds that her argument is aesthetic rather than moral?'

'It's not clear,' Professor Honderich says, 'that it would be an argument of any sort. Consider a man who argues that the fundamental moral principle is to maximize the colour mauve. Under questioning, he admits that mauve doesn't make people happy, issue an injustice or whatever, but maintains that one should maximize it none the less *just* because it is intrinsically good. Such a moral principle would seem incredible. Indeed, it is difficult to see that it is a moral principle at all.

'However, it is not obvious what stands between it and *any* non-consequentialist moral principle – for instance, that one should always act according to the will of a supernatural being. Such principles seem as dubiously moral as your sister Bobo's arguments for prohibiting hard drugs – not that she's offered any.'

I'm greatly obliged to Professor Honderich but will not include this brief tutorial, I think, when I write my memoirs. It would be quite wrong to allow my sister Bobo to be refuted behind her back and without giving her an opportunity to muster her case more cogently.

I had just arrived at this conclusion when my favourite of her children, my niece Claudia, telephones to ask me how the lunch had gone.

'Mother was so looking forward to it,' she says. 'She could hardly wait to tell you about some cricketer who'd died.'

'A *cricketer*. Your mother has never cared about cricket.'

'That's what I thought,' says Claudia. 'He was called Davies, I think. She wanted to tell you that he'd died. "Well, ring him now," I said. "Oh no, I couldn't do that," she said. "I wouldn't want to interrupt his work." Did she mention him?'

'I think she may have have done,' I say, 'but I had no idea who he was. She does rather hang on to the past, your mother.'

'Oh dear,' says Claudia. 'She was so happy that she'd remembered who he was. She will be disappointed.'

Claudia sounds disappointed too, and I'm not surprised. On summer holidays in Broadstairs, when I was twelve or so and my sister Bobo fourteen, I insisted, since cricket was my greatest interest at the time, that the whole family attend every day of Canterbury week. My sister Bobo, who had ambitions only to become a musical comedy *ingénue* in the manner of Binnie Hale or, if nothing came of that, to marry Alan Ladd, was lugged along even though she wouldn't have known a Kent cricketer from a bar of soap – least of all J. G. W. Davies, a prep-school master who turned out occasionally in August and fielded enthusiastically at cover-point.

And yet, forty years on, an obituary – probably in the *Daily Telegraph* – had stirred some memory of a shared and not to be devalued past – of long, carefree summer days when everything had seemed all right, when she had hoped to be an *ingénue* and I'd imagined that I'd play for England. And, believing in continuity, she had wanted urgently to share this memory with me. And so I'd disappointed her.

I have no particular excuse, other than that I see no point in looking back. Happy memories, since everything is over, hurt more than sad ones. Nor does my wife seem to understand this any more clearly than my sister Bobo does. She, too, hangs on to the past; will suddenly remind me on the telephone – quite innocently, quite without malice, I think – of something nice that happened fifteen years ago.

I don't want to be reminded that my wife was happy once. When *The Henry Root Letters* went straight to number one, and since I was able briefly to be generous (wishing to repay my wife, perhaps, for the fact that she'd been kind to me for the past ten years), I took her for six weeks to Ibiza.

We went by car and she – believing at last, perhaps, that there was some justice after all – smiled happily all the way. And she wore a summer hat that didn't suit her in the least and the hat blew off and, feeling safe at last, she laughed and held my hand, and she was happy, I think, for the next six weeks; believed, perhaps, that this was how it would always be; that she could trust me to be kind to her; that we might grow old together.

I don't want to be reminded of this; nor do I want to be reminded of August afternoons when J. G. W. Davies turned out for Kent and fielded keenly in the covers. I don't want to look back at all – a habit of mind which may serve me ill when I write my memoirs.

Searching for memoir material in my files, I discover a very nice letter from Bernard Delfont, posted some months before his death, in which he thanks me for something I'd written about him in the *Independent*. I'm not in the least surprised by this small courtesy, nor by the enclosed request that I ring him up and suggest a day when I might be free for lunch. Like most successful people Delfont always had time to be kind to others. Equally, he was always available on the telephone. These days, young people who have never received a necessary phone call in their lives have insulting intercept devices attached to the apparatus and will, after a minute or so, bunk you off in favour of someone else. No one as busy and serious as Delfont was would ever bunk you off for someone else, no matter who they were.

Nor would my friend Michael O'Mara, the brilliant young publisher, with whom I had lunch today. Like Delfont O'Mara is never in a meeting, tied up, visiting Frankfurt or on the other line – and while lunch can last from twelve to five bestsellers continue to drop as if by magic off the assembly line.

It isn't magic, of course. O'Mara simply has his priorities right, understanding that personnel can keep the machinery running while he talks serious matters through with me. Which isn't to say that he hasn't used me in the past to – as he'd put it – make a buck.

O'Mara's thoroughly deserved fortune is based securely on a clutch of highly successful Royal books, not least *Diana – Her True Story*, by Andrew Morton, which, as he'd be the first to admit, would never, but for me, have come his way. Aware of my slight connection with the Royal Family (based on little more, in fact, than my having been a member in the fifties of the Princess Margaret set and my later acquaintance with the Princess of Wales), he asked me one day to obtain Diana's cooperation with Andrew Morton's book, which, of course, I was delighted to do.

That's in the past, however. Our present friendship is underpinned not by commercial advantage but by a shared world view or 'philosophy' (more or less, that if you can get your tight end to pancake two defensive linemen you're in for a touchdown), and the only curiosity is how we reached this position (this identical assumption of what is an appropriate role for a man) via such different routes.

While I, aged ten, was being coached privately at cricket by Geary of Leicestershire and England ('Ready when you are, Master William'), and later, dressed in plus-fours exactly like my father's and equipped with a twelve-bore larger than myself, was blasting sitting ducks into kingdom come, O'Mara was stealing hubcaps on the streets of Philadelphia and, later, working his way through college as a part-time parking valet.

So much for nurture you might suppose; nature's the controlling influence, and it's tempting to suppose that O'Mara and I have reached this shared and unflinching 'masculinity', this assumption of a morality most usually associated, perhaps, with the locker-room of a blue-collar American football team, through a similar genetic inheritance.

Tempting but wrong, I think. A more careful analysis would show that the lessons taught in Sunningdale – get out there, take the lumps, kick arse and don't complain – are also taught on the streets of Philadelphia. Counselling and support groups, trick-cyclists and sordid introspection are no more encouraged in Philadelphia than they are in Sunningdale.

In a nutshell, O'Mara and I are both 'real men'. That said, we have agreed – for our own amusement – that he's slightly more 'real' than me; that he, for my benefit, should present a hard image over lunch unattainable by me; that he should tell stories the point of which is to make my eyes pop.

Today he comes up with one of his best. For some weeks, he says, he has been pestered by Lew Stichler, a contact from the old days.

'He was a film producer once,' O'Mara says. 'A big-time windbag. A suitcase full of projects. Revolving credit. Lorimar on the other line. A mug five times before lunch. Recently he lost it all – his money, his house, his wife, his children. Now he scrapes a living pushing giveaway magazines through letter-boxes.'

'How awful.'

'Right,' says O'Mara 'I've been avoiding him, of course, but he caught me for lunch the other day. I tried to get out of it. I didn't want to listen to his troubles for two hours. In the event I was amazed. He looked ghastly, he'd aged ten years and he walked with a stick.'

'Appalling.'

'Indeed. But here's the point: he wasn't sorry for himself. On the way to lunch he said: "I'm back on my feet." Then a gust of wind blew him clean into the gutter. He lay on his back *laughing*.'

'Magnificent!' I say. 'He was in the gutter, but he was looking at the stars.'

'Precisely. He'd discovered, through adversity, who he really was.'

'He'd been to hell and back.'

'He'd lost *everything*,' O'Mara says, 'except his self-respect. For the first time in his life he really *liked* himself.'

'A lesson to us all,' I say. 'Because he wasn't sorry for himself you'll be happy to see him again.'

O'Mara looks astonished. 'Why should I want to see him again? The man's a loser.'

I rock with laughter. 'One door closes and another door closes! Some more Rioja, do you think?'

And later I give O'Mara another opportunity to play his part. Some years ago, I say, Coral Browne was in a play at Her Majesty's produced by Emile Littler. During the run her husband, Philip Pearman, died. Rather nervously Miss Browne asked Littler whether she could skip a matinée to bury him. To her surprise, Littler agreed. But when she received her pay-packet that week she noticed that it had been docked one performance.

O'Mara stares at me. 'Yes?' he says.

'Yes what?'

'I don't understand the story,' he says. 'What's the point?'

'Her husband had just died, for God's sake, and Littler *charged* her for missing the matinée!'

O'Mara concentrates furiously for a few seconds, frowns, drums his fingers on the table and then gives up.

'Sorry,' he says. 'I don't get it. I don't understand the joke.'

I now tell him that I'm to stand bail tomorrow for the rightful King of Spain; further that I plan to wear my Sunday suit and, as I always do when standing bail, my old Wykehamist tie. At which point, and rather to my surprise, O'Mara advises caution.

'You don't think I should stand bail? You doubt this chap's credentials?'

'No, it isn't that,' O'Mara says. 'I wouldn't question your assessment of the situation. I merely meant that you might be advised not to wear your Old Wykehamist tie.'

Then he tells me a very curious story. When he was at the start of his career in publishing, the board of the company he worked for engaged as sales director a man who, in O'Mara's judgement, was an obvious phoney. O'Mara expressed his doubts to the board about the way this chap presented himself – inauthentic upper-class accent, threadbare anecdotes, Old Wykehamist tie – but the managing director suggested that O'Mara, as an American, was hardly an expert judge in matters of background. But O'Mara was vindicated. Sure enough, and within a matter of weeks, this soi-disant gent disappeared with all the takings.

'Well done,' I say. 'You twigged him. All bogus, his background?'

'Not at all,' O'Mara said. 'He had been to Winchester.'

That's too subtle for me, and I resolve, in any case, to wear my Old Wykehamist tie in court tomorrow. Then, remembering the point of these meetings nowadays, I ask O'Mara whether he'd like to hear the anecdote concerning J. P. Donleavy's *Fairy Tales of New York* and my attempt, in 1961, to defraud Sir Donald Albery.

'The play survived the coldest winter since records were first kept,' I say, 'and I thought that if we could just keep it running until April when the tourists could be expected we would eventually . . .'

'Good heavens! Is that the time?' O'Mara says. 'I ought to get back to the office.'

Later at home I brood about this conversation – about the unfortunate Mr Stichler, about Emile Littler, about ruthlessness and business ethics generally, concluding at last that if you can't be honest your only option is to be dishonourable within the law.

Like Pigge the Banker. Pigge the Banker wanted to try his hand at producing, so I rented him the Comedy, on which I had a lease at the time, for some play whose name I've quite forgotten. It was a dog, a real turkey, opening to the worst reviews I've ever read and attracting an audience of just three people on its second night.

Had I been Pigge the Banker, and recognizing that the game was up, I'd have done the difficult thing: I'd have left the country. Pigge the Banker took the easy way out. Instead of paying me the four weeks' rent he owed he mustered several hundredweight of theatrical solicitors, thereafter instructing them to search for a loophole in the contract.

In due course, one of these wrote me a letter in which he claimed that, because the Comedy was being used in the daytime by a troupe called 'Shakespeare for Schools', it was unavailable to Pigge the Banker for rehearsals after his play had opened. This circumstance, he said, was why the play had failed.

Shockingly threadbare stuff, even by a lawyer's standards, and when the matter eventually went to arbitration in front of Lord Goodman I expected His Lordship, with one slight shift of his towering moral weight, to squash Pigge the Banker as flat as a dab.

Which, after about five seconds of the hearing, is exactly what he did – instructing Pigge the Banker to cough up pronto. He didn't, however, call him a shifty little twister or rebuke his solicitor – which was not surprising, I suppose, since he and Pigge had only tried to swindle me *within the law*.

I tried to be ruthless once, but it didn't work. In 1964 Michael White and I were planning to co-produce *Nights at the Comedy*, a bold attempt to revive music hall in the West End. One week, when Michael was on holiday in Paris, I dropped in on Bernard Delfont at his spookily carpeted and low-lit office above the Prince of Wales. In those days I often dropped in on Delfont, and he was grateful for the company, I think, since his only other visitor seemed to be his heart physician, who always called at teatime.

While the consultant took stethoscope soundings of his distinguished and shirtless patient's breathing, I outlined my plans for *Nights at the Comedy* – putting particular emphasis on one spectacular coup: we had persuaded Nicol Williamson, then the golden boy of the British theatre, to compère the show.

Delfont, who had not heard of Williamson, I think, told his

physician to suspend his soundings for a while, thereafter, and using the only telephone on his enormous desk, checking out Williamson's credentials with his unseen long-time sidekick Billy Marsh.

Mr Marsh must have given Williamson the thumbs-up, since Delfont then offered to finance the show entirely himself, on just one condition: that he should co-produce it with me. I didn't hesitate. I agreed on the spot – feeling as if I'd come of age, as if this was the way grown-up businessmen behaved – and I greatly enjoyed telling Michael White that Delfont was in and he was out; I got quite a kick out of this piece of random cruelty to a friend.

It reminded me of a time at Winchester when I had dropped my best friend, Simon Gourlay, just for the hell of it. Gourlay had a round face and curly hair, and I suddenly thought it would be amusing – might make life less boring for a moment – randomly to drop him. He was utterly bewildered; he begged me to be friends still; he cried a bit – and that did excite me. I had supposed that I'd grown morally since then, but the kick I got out of Michael White's bewilderment showed me that I hadn't.

I didn't get away with it, of course. You have to be far better organized, far more self-believing, than I ever was to get away with behaviour such as this. You have to have the will of a criminal or resolve never to behave like this again. Alternatively, and like Pigge the Banker, you have to be dishonourable within the law. The effect on me was that I was never able to take myself seriously again.

Michael White went to see his lawyer, the ever-resourceful Oscar Beuselink, who had a word with Delfont on the telephone. I then received a letter from Delfont, returning the investor's agreement and pointing out, quite kindly, that he didn't wish to be the cause of a falling-out between such good friends as Michael and myself.

It was too late to raise money from another quarter, and the show must have broken some sort of record by being the first to be mounted entirely with a credit card. In the event, it contained many marvels, including Ida Barr, Princess Juanita and her snakes,

Demetrius the Gladiator, a man who sang 'Mule Train' while hitting himself over the head with a tin tray and, most memorably, Mrs Shufflewick.

Not, however, Nicol Williamson, who went absent two days before the opening night – a consequence of a long evening I spent with him in Soho. As we moved from pub to pub Williamson became lachrymose and fighting mad by turns – one minute bewailing the fact that Sarah Miles, infuriated, I think, by his incompetence in a fist-fight (forever inviting small Irishmen on to the cobbles and being laid out flat himself), had recently dropped him from her arrangements; the next vowing that he'd get her back again.

'She'll discover her mistake!' he roared. 'She'll not find another man like me! She'll not replace me with some fucking public-school johnnie twit-faced shit!'

Since I had just taken up residence with Miss Miles, but judged that it would be tactless and boastful to say as much, I maintained a sympathetic silence while Williamson raved on, and the next day, having discovered the truth – and feeling foolish, I supposed – he walked out of the show.

It suffered other setbacks too. Demetrius the Gladiator, whose forte was blowing up hot-water bottles, experienced a loss of wind on the first night, breathed in when he should have breathed out and was blown twenty feet backwards into a brick wall. Mrs Shufflewick, taking advantage of the fact that the stage had been converted into a pub interior dispensing real alcohol, got drunk after her turn and refused to exit, preferring to remain on stage and offer a derisive running commentary on the quality of the other acts, some of which she judged to be better than others. Lowest in her estimation was Princess Juanita and her snakes. 'Don't put your snakes on the stage, Mrs Worthington,' said Mrs Shufflewick, causing Princess Juanita to have a tantrum and, later, to leave the show.

The worst misfortune, however, was the result of my decision to engage the services of Arthur Howard, who had been a contender once for the British middleweight title, and to offer £5 to any member of the audience who could box him on the nose. Having been assured that Arthur, whose fists, since he was a professional fighter, were classified for legal purposes as offensive weapons, wouldn't hit back, a sailor from Plymouth climbed on stage and immediately caught Arthur a terrific crack plum on the button. Arthur, who was a bit punchy, forgot the no-retaliation guarantee and chased the sailor round the stage, finally catching him in a corner and giving him a frightful whacking.

I dispensed with Arthur's services and instead engaged a Mr Wladek Kowalski, a 25-stone wrestler who normally bounced for Charlie and Eddie Richardson. Mr Kowalski announced from the stage that he could withstand any blow to the abdomen, however hard.

'I'm as strong as an ox!' he cried.

A small man in a dinner-jacket climbed on stage and boxed him in the stomach. Mr Kowalski collapsed on the spot and died a few hours later from peritonitis – this accident giving rise to some friction thereafter between myself and the Richardson brothers, which was only was only repaired when I palled up, years later, with Frankie Fraser.

The show closed after eight weeks and I went down for some £15,000 – quite a lot of money in those days, though not, I think, to Bernard Delfont. When I went to see him with the news he was so startled that his heart physician thought it best to take another sounding.

'One hundred and fifty thousand pounds, Bill!' said Delfont. 'You can't go down for as little as that!'

'Not £150,000,' I said; '£15,000.'

Delfont couldn't get his brain round this piece of information in the least – not understanding, perhaps, that they don't, at Winchester, teach you how to handle such a shortfall. Eventually, he found his voice.

'I don't know, Bill,' he said. 'When I started in the business I couldn't have told you on any particular day whether I had £15,000 in the bank or was £15,000 in the red. You should have come to me. I'd have helped you out.'

He would have done, I think, but it was too late by then to repair the damage. He did teach me one valuable lesson, however: that you have no place in business if you can't imagine your way out of a shortfall of a mere £15,000. And unlike Sir Donald Albery, say, he did everything he could to help.

I dropped in on Albery to explain the situation, cleared my throat, took a deep breath and said: 'I'm afraid I'm going bust for . . .'

At which point, and before I was halfway through the sentence, he telephoned his lawyers, elicited an opinion, disputed the price of same, reached a compromise, summoned a secretary and dictated a letter under the complicated terms of which I made the management fee in *Beyond the Fringe* over to him.

'. . . £15,000,' I said.

'Have a cup of tea,' he said.

Delfont, by contrast, took the lease of the Comedy Theatre off my hands and insisted thereafter that all the profits from letting it to other managements should go to me – even though I was quite unentitled to them.

Delfont was a kind man, and now, reading his letter again, I rather wish I'd had the courtesy to answer it. He wouldn't have minded my anecdotes, I think; he might even have sat still for the one in which I tried to defraud Sir Donald Albery. Feeling rather sad I return his letter to the file.

To court with Black Simone to stand bail for the King of Spain – an outing I'd intended to miss on the grounds that our man is obviously, and as charged, a minor local fraudsman and Black Simone as mad as a bag of spanners. But then I'd thought, no, I must summon up the energy; material for my memoirs might be forthcoming, so I take my place in the chauffeur-driven limo which Black Simone has hired for the occasion. Although His Majesty makes do with a life-long bus pass, Black Simone explains, he would expect us to arrive by car.

'He's not flash on his own account,' says Black Simone. 'He's like those Dutch bicycle-ridin' Royals.'

Seeing an opportunity here for an apropos anecdote, I mention my friend David Conyers and his production of *Hair* in Amsterdam. And that was an odd business, though not entirely unexpected. Conyers was a bright young agent who, after the Music Corporation of America was closed down by the US anti-trust laws, set up London Management with Robin Fox. Then he had the first of many nervous breakdowns. One minute he was as right as ninepence and the next he got drunk at lunchtime and threw his secretary out of the window. Fox put him into a psychiatric home and later, when he was heavily sedated, induced him to surrender his shares in the agency to him.

When he was discharged from the psychiatric home he came to see me and suggested that we set up an agency together. I liked the look of him, so I agreed – notwithstanding the fact that he was kept going by electro-convulsive shock therapy powered by a pocket dynamo hidden under his waistcoat.

Everything went excellently for a week or two and then he threw my friend Lady Leighton out of the window. I put him back into the psychiatric home, later, and when he was heavily sedated, persuading him to sign his share of the agency over to me. A bit of an up-and-down career, as I now explain to Black Simone.

'One day,' I say, 'the batteries failed in his pocket dynamo and, as a consequence, he forgot to book a theatre in Amsterdam for his production of *Hair*. However, he did remember to invite the Dutch Royal Family to the first night.

'A circus tent was hired and bench seats hastily erected. These, unfortunately, were balanced incorrectly, causing a see-saw effect. When the Dutch Royal Family arrived the audience stood up and the Dutch Royal Family sat down. Then the audience sat down and the Dutch Royal Family were shot into the air like tumblers on a variety bill. When the band played the Dutch national anthem the audience stood up and the Dutch Royal Family were sent sprawling in the sawdust. This might have gone on all night had not Dutch creditors – solemn men with briefcases and *aides-mémoire* – arrived to take the set away.

'Alternatively, you might like to hear about my attempt in 1961 to defraud Sir Donald Albery. J. P. Donleavy's *Fairy Tales of New York* had just opened at the Comedy . . .'

'Oh look,' says Black Simone. 'That must be the court-house over there.'

Ten minutes later we're in the foyer of the court, where I discover to my surprise that Black Simone has managed to obtain the services of a perfectly sensible-looking barrister to argue our man's case. Nor does the barrister show any obvious signs that he takes us to be mad. It's not a barrister's job, I suppose, to ridicule his client and his client's friends, but it does surprise me that he can keep a straight face while Black Simone seeks to persuade him that our man, far from being a small-time fraudsman charged with impersonation and obtaining goods on credit (the accounts to be sent to Buckingham Palace), is HRH Prince Don Juan Alfonso, the eldest son of King Alfonso XIII and Queen Eugenie Victoria. In the circumstances, and in case our barrister should suppose that I'm off my rocker too, I now pull faces and wink at him behind Black Simone's back – a performance I hastily discontinue when our brief looks at me warily, as if I might be the only idiot here.

'Because His Royal Highness turned out to be black,' Black Simone explains, 'his nanny was told to dispose of him in a planned incident. Instead, she smuggled him to Nicaragua, where he was protected by Somoza. Later he was brought to England, where he was kept in the basement at Windsor Castle with the White Russians. While the authorities were unsure which way Franco would jump, they treated him well enough, but when the impostor, Juan Carlos, was nominated King, they dropped him like a hot potato. His business people were withdrawn and he fell into the hands of hoodlums.'

It's the first I've heard of hoodlums – and it's the first our sensible-looking barrister has heard of hoodlums, too, I think. Perhaps this will persuade him to gather up his papers and return to London – there to seek consolation in a cup of tea, a digestive biscuit and a word with his clerk. 'Odd case, Smithers. A man claiming the be the King of Spain, a large black woman dressed as if for carnival week in Rio and a craggy senior, more or less all there I'd have thought, and wearing an Old Wykehamist tie . . .'

Not a bit of it. '*Hoodlums?*' he says. 'What hoodlums, precisely?'

'Mrs Ferguson,' says Black Simone.

'Mrs *Ferguson*? Who's Mrs Ferguson?'

'A black woman,' says Black Simone scornfully, 'who considers herself to be at the pinnacle of Ealing society. Mrs Ferguson thought it would do her no harm socially to be seen runnin' around Ealing with the King of Spain.'

Our sensible barrister obviously agrees with this, and seconds later we're all in court. Here I get my first sighting of His Majesty, whose general aspect does nothing, from where I'm sitting, to persuade me that he's the King of Spain. He looks, frankly, like the quite shady relief *sommelier* at a Third World embassy. The magistrate, on the other hand, is an erect, silvery-haired old party with the decent look of a man who might once have lost a Spitfire over Germany, thereafter ending up in Colditz as a bolshie misfit. I'll be all right here, I think. The magistrate and I will communicate on some paralinguistic level – inaccessible to my associates in court – thereby identifying each other as almost equals through the deep grammar of a shared background. *Almost* equals, since the conditioning facts of my life – Winchester, the Navy, Cambridge – will be mutually recognized as crucially superior to his: Harrow, Oxford and the RAF.

When it is my turn to take the stand I do so with some confidence. I'm a little surprised, therefore, when after I've revealed that I'm a writer the magistrate draws back slightly on the bench and looks at me warily, as if I might be a bomb in a shopping-bag. He then observes that writing is a very hazardous business; further, and because the prosecution is looking for two sureties in the sum of £5,000 each, that I could, in the event of His Majesty absconding, lose my house.

'I haven't got a house,' I say.

The magistrate is thunderstruck. 'You haven't got a *house*? Where on earth do you live?'

'In a flat.'

'In a *flat*?' The magistrate draws back slightly and places a hand over his heart. 'What do you do with your rubbish?'

'Stick it outside the door,' I say. 'What do you do with yours?'

As a general rule I wouldn't have been so pert, but I'm becoming irritated. I'm only here to help a crew of obvious fantasists and yet this Old Harrovian Spitfire pilot is treating me as if it's me who's crackers.

What am I up against here? Some atavistic unease with supposed class treachery? I am reminded of some cautionary remarks by my friend Paul Foot. I happened to tell him that I had bet Val Hennessy £500 that I was commoner than her. 'You were born common,' I told her, 'none commoner, perhaps – but I have *become* common.' Foot said I was playing with fire. 'The Lord Chief Justice once fined me £500 for being common,' he said, 'and threatened me with a gaol sentence. They don't like you being common.' Perhaps the magistrate is going to lock me up. Be that as it may, I never discover what he does with his rubbish since he is too bewildered by my lifestyle to give an answer. He shakes his head and then he asks me where I work.

'The *Independent*,' I say. I should leave it at that, but, wishing to be taken a bit more seriously here, I add that I also write books.

'Books?' The magistrate doesn't like the sound of this at all. '*Books?* What books?'

'My first,' I say, 'was a picaresque novel called *Both the Ladies and the Gentlemen*. You'll have no difficulty with the sly, but appropriate, borrowing from Auden. "In a brothel/Both the ladies and the gentlemen/Have nicknames only." And then I wrote . . .'

I suspend this proposed inventory of my stuff out of deference to the fact that the magistrate appears to be having a cardiac arrest. He's rocking backwards and forwards on the bench, gasping and wheezing and fighting for breath – this performance being identifiable in due course as a prelude to a witticism.

'I see,' he manages to say at last. 'More *trollop* than Trollope!'

Oh for fuck's sake. But then I think, no, every cloud, etc. Thanks to this buffoonish observation, an idea for a Christmas toilet book has dropped fully formed into my mind. *How to Tell If Your Parents Aren't on Drugs*. No one on drugs would ever say 'More trollop than Trollope!' – not, at least, after due thought and in a public place – and I'm so busy composing the next few entries in my head (the majority drawn from conversations with various Pratleys down the years) that I have to be called to order by the clerk.

'Do you understand?' he says.

'Sorry? Understand what?'

'I have just ruled,' the magistrate says, 'that because of the hazardous nature of your profession I will only accept a surety from you in the sum of £5,000 if it is guaranteed by your bank manager. You may step down.'

I doubt whether my bank manager, whom I've never met, will oblige on this score – not that this worries me unduly since I assume that the magistrate, once he has listened to Black Simone, will bang His Majesty up and throw away the keys. Not a bit of it. Black Simone, who's on next, clearly impresses the court when she says she's happy to take the odds against HRH Don Juan Alfonso pitching up when next required.

'And who are you?' the magistrate asks.

'Black Simone,' says Black Simone. 'The *Independent*. Lifestyle and Home Affairs.'

'Do you own a house?'

'No, m'lud,' says Black Simone. 'But I do have wheels.'

'Which is more than your editor seems to have,' the magistrate observes.

This unnecessary insult from the bench is almost too much. First my work is mocked and now I'm sneered at for a present lack of wheels. I'm about to point out that Black Simone's wheels are, in any case, on hire by the hour – the account to be forwarded later, I imagined, and along with His Majesty's other obligations, to the Queen at Buckingham Palace. I decide, however, to maintain a haughty silence.

'Thank you, m'lud,' Black Simone continues. 'In the circumstances I'm prepared to slap five K on the table which says our man will appear next week. And I'll tell you this, m'lud: I'm sixty–forty he's the fucking King.'

That's it, I think, I'm in the clear. Black Simone will be banged up for contempt, the King will be committed and the rest of us will be sent packing. Not a bit of it. The magistrate rules that he'll gladly accept Black Simone's surety in the sum of £5,000 – his only regret being that he'll have to keep His Majesty in custody until I come up with the other five. Worse, and once we've been dismissed, I discover that, since the King's continuing confinement is taken to be my fault, I am now expected to visit my bank manager as soon as possible.

Stuff that. I'm not going to make an idiot of myself by running into my bank and asking the manager to lend me £5,000 so that I can stand bail for a man who is no more the King of Spain than I am. My relations with the Midland Bank, Sloane Square, have always been excellent and I don't intend to spoil them now.

Not that I say all, or any, of this to Black Simone and our man's barrister. I see no reason to depress them at the moment. It would be kinder to let them become increasingly bewildered as the days go by and they find I neither take their calls nor ring them back. I tell them, therefore, that they have nothing to worry about; that I'll visit my bank early in the morning; that we'll have sprung the King within a week, no problem. They'll become increasingly distraught as the days go by and I ignore their calls – but that's their fault, frankly.

Black Simone should never have involved me in the first place. She should have shown me more respect. Would she have involved old Bill Deedes or Sir Peregrine Worsthorne? I think not. She took advantage of me because, being kind, I tend to treat people like her as equals. Now she must learn that she is merely cabaret; to be used briefly as a joke and then returned to limbo.

Not that I'll put it quite like this if I include the incident in my memoirs. As I explained to my hairdresser Miss Vicky, I won't want to come across in these as mean-minded or superior; nor, which would stylistically be worse, will I want boastfully to present myself (in order to get marks for candour) in an unbecoming light.

I continue to seethe inwardly at the way I was treated yesterday in court. Rather to my surprise I'm more disturbed by the magistrate's failure to recognize me as his social superior than I was when a group of us from the Tiger Aspect office attended Justin Judd's wedding on a Norfolk lawn and the butler, mistaking us for circus folk, locked us in the servants' hall.

I'm not particularly snobbish, I think, but I have always supposed that – notwithstanding the fact that one hasn't moved in such circles for thirty years – one would be instantly accepted in the milieu of one's birth. Wondering now whether one could, if one so wished, reacquaint oneself with this milieu's mysteries, with its code words and mealtime nuances, I am struck by an idea for a television show.

There is a current series on BBC2, called *My Secret Life* or something of the sort, in which shadowy participants own up to vaguely shameful occasional enthusiasms. Thus, an accountant will admit that he likes to go shoplifting once a week; a scaggy-looking couple who work for a building society will reveal themselves as serial Friday-night orgiasts.

Participating first in my everyday hat – as a perfectly respectable crack-taker and familiar of common, sharp-faced women – I will then expose myself (*sotto voce*) as an occasional, and secret, visitor to White's and Boodles. I will first be filmed at ease in Happy's crack-house, then, later, treading furtively down the shadowy road to Boodles in St James's – coat-collar turned up, hat pulled down over my eyes – where, in case tooled-up yardies might, by following me, discover my shameful secret, I will look to left and right before diving suddenly inside.

It's a first-class idea, I think, and I shall pitch it to my new friend Jonty Agnew when next we speak. Agnew, a thrusting young independent, is six foot six inches tall (the minimum height for a good producer, I've always thought) with the confident manner and clear complexion of a man of action. Whether, like Justin Judd – and covered in blood and feathers – he always carries a twelve-bore into meetings or, like Judd, had never until he was thirty-one eaten lamb which hadn't been killed on his own estates, I'm not quite sure. This much is obvious, however: he's not at all the type suddenly to start blubbing at the Groucho Club or be duffed up by a fat man from Central Television. He'll fight my corner. I and my concept will be safe with him.

And now, while I wait for the Publisher to return to our table, I decide that my old friend Pratley wants me to score him some grass. This surprises me. Notwithstanding his occasional unpaid employment in an old-time jazz combo originally formed at Oxford, this particular Pratley has, in my opinion, always kept the cork rather too tightly in the bottle. Happily married with four children, he brews his own beer and has with his own hands recently built an extension to his house in W11, which he lets to student nurses. On Friday nights, he will, if the combo's leader asks him, play the trumpet on a pub podium in Battersea – but otherwise he keeps his nose clean.

Pratley explains on the telephone that the stuff isn't for him but for Godber, the combo's drummer. Godber had previously kept himself going with cough mixtures and Do-Do's, but now he wanted to experiment with something stronger.

'I owe Godber a favour,' says Pratley, 'and I'm at my wits' end. If you can't help I'll have to go to Brixton, and that's the last thing I want to do. I'm told it's far from safe these days.'

As it happens, Pratley's in luck. After her last visit Jillypoo left some grass behind. I tell Pratley that he's welcome to this; that he should meet me in Macmillans in the Fulham Road at six o'clock, when I'll hand it over.

Pratley almost sobs with gratitude. 'You've saved my life,' he says. 'Wild horses couldn't have taken me to Brixton.'

The pleasure's mine, in fact. Pratley, I decide, can help me with my memoirs. It will balance the book nicely, I think, if there is one boring old party in it who will listen to my anecdotes. This particular Pratley will be admirable in this walk-on role.

'I'll come prepared with anecdotes,' I say. 'Which do you prefer? Naval or theatrical? The time my submarine was 287 miles off course during a Nato exercise and suddenly popped up like a cork in a yachting complex in Copenhagen? Or would you prefer my attempt to defraud Sir Donald Albery? In 1961, *Fairy Tales of New York* opened to excellent reviews and I . . .'

'I think I'll go to Brixton,' says Pratley, and he hangs up on me.

Hurt and confused, I might at this point have reached for the Rohypnols, recently delivered by Honest John, but instead I crack my knuckles and walk around, and then I get busy in the kitchen. At which point, Pratley rings back.

'What are you doing?' he says.

'Cooking,' I say.

I assume that he wants to apologize; that he's still in search of some grass and would rather listen to one of my anecdotes than go to Brixton. Not a bit of it. He wants me to introduce him to Saffy the Page Three Scorcher, to take her to to pub in Battersea where, on Friday nights, he plays the trumpet.

What's wrong with these musicians? Why can't they get it together for themselves? Pratley's a good-looking man and a half-decent trumpeter so why can't he find his own girls? When June Upstairs lived above us she had pop musicians queueing round the clock – most memorably a family entertainer from America (justly celebrated for the excellence of his Christmas Specials) who got a vibrator stuck up his arse one night and needed medical assistance. And June Upstairs was no oil painting even then.

If Saffy agrees to the rendezvous Pratley will be the sixth musician at least to whom I've introduced her. Not that this will do him any good. She's lovely, Saffy, still as pretty as a picture, still wheeled on in gossip columns for old times' sake (bitten by a camel on location, taken up photography, lost her cat, gone mad, that sort of thing), but she's been celibate for twenty years.

Not that I tell Pratley this. I say I'll give her a ring and if she agrees to the rendezvous I'll bring her to the pub in Battersea on Friday week. Then Pratley happens to say that he's just been speaking on the telephone to our mutual friend Pratley. According to Pratley, Pratley thinks I'm not respectable, indeed that I'm thoroughly corrupt.

'He wishes to have nothing more to do with you,' says Pratley.

I'm quite upset that Pratley should have come to this opinion – and without just cause, as far as I can see. I return to the kitchen, where, happily, the harmless activity of cooking soon calms me down. Cooking's half the fun. Measuring, mixing, stirring, getting the balance of ingredients exactly right, warming the promising soup over a gentle flame – anxiously waiting for the lumps to form. 'The lumps,' as my friend Professor Steve Jones said on television recently, 'are what make life interesting.'

I've done well on this occasion. In no time at all a huge oil slick appears in the spoon, shortly thereafter forming into a rock the size of a croquet ball. Jillypoo, in spite of domestic worries of her own, has come up trumps. When she delivered earlier, she said she'd just complained to the council about her housing subsidence.

'You mean subsistence,' I said.

'No I don't,' she said. 'I mean subsidence. The house is sinking.'

We'll be all right tomorrow night, me and my baby. Life will be as interesting as it can be. We'll excel ourselves. I wish sometimes that I had another choice, but there's nothing else I want. I knew at the age of twenty that the rewards for good behaviour, while real and obvious, would never be enough – or, more accurately, would be too much; a burden rather than a solace. I knew that if you cherished nothing, nothing you cherished could be taken away. Addiction seems usually to be a form of cowardice.

Whether, long term, there's something else for Penny – the world of prams and bicycles, of simple endurance and other people's wives, of commitments undertaken and duties honourably discharged, and, in spite of all this, a death sentence, in the end, delivered in a cold room ('I'm sorry to have to tell you that your wife . . .') – I'm still not sure. In a way, I hope there might be, since if there is she's not at risk. Only those who are destroyed already – for whom there's nothing anyway – are at any risk from drugs: people who, when they should be doing something nice, find it less boring to run the gauntlet of scarred women in a crack-house or cruise Hammersmith at 2 a.m. and give a blowjob to a biker.

Five years ago I'd have said it was odds on my baby would, sooner or later, take refuge with a fat man who was kind to her, might live in a cold seaside town, dine out in an Italian restaurant once a week and laugh at a tradesman's jokes. Now I'm not so sure. Behind the joyful laugh and level gaze there might be a sense of nothingness, I think, which means she's mine.

And, later, I'm still brooding about this when Pratley rings back.

'I'm greatly concerned,' he says, 'by what you might write about me in your memoirs.'

'Don't worry,' I say. 'I won't mention you at all.'

'Thank you,' says Pratley. 'I'm a happily married man.'

'Of course.'

'Don't forget to ring up Saffy the Page Three Scorcher.'

THURSDAY 10.47 p.m.

What? You want to know what?

'Golly! What your biggest disaster was. You said, don't you want to know what my biggest disaster was, and so I said yes of *course* I do. Golly!'

Good.

'So?'

So what?

'What was it?'

What was what?

'Christ! Your biggest disaster. What was it?'

Oh that. Sorry. Brain not working.

'I know what you mean. It's good, this.'

Fucking good.

'You all right?'

Absolutely.

'What happened to that idea of yours? I liked that one. It was brilliant. I know it was.'

What idea? I had an idea?

'Definitely. For television. Your secret life, or something. Having dinner at that place.'

Boodles.

'Right! Boodles. It was *really* good. I liked that one.'

I was let down.

'*No!* Who by?'

Jonty Agnew.

'But you said he was great. You said he was six foot six.'

And so he is. I was quite excited. I rang him every day. I could never get through. He was always in a meeting. I was impressed. This is good, I thought. He's a busy man. Pitching, lying, taking meetings. Then he asked *me* to a meeting.

'Wow!'

Exactly. I was immensely bucked. I set the alarm. Dressed accordingly. Got there early. Odd venue. Sparsely furnished. Coffee in plastic cups. Mad women. Distracted men. But a reassuring sprinkling of celebrated faces. Anthony Hopkins. Henrietta Moraes. Michael Barrymore. Paul Merson, the little striker. I was impressed.

'I bet.'

I buttonholed Sir Hopkins. 'You have a development?' I said.

'I'm in recovery,' he said. I was at an AA meeting. Jonty's a recovering addict.

'Oh dear. It must be awful, that.'

Frightful. He's six foot six and he's in recovery. I ask you.

'Dreadful. Can I have another? A real whopper?'

Here.

'What did you do?'

I left. Then Jonty rang me up. 'Can I share?' he said. He's a producer and he wanted to share!

'Fucking cheek!'

Right! I should have said, 'You cunt! You're a producer! Send me the fucking cheque!'

'*Absolutely.* Your turn.'

Thanks. Plus, he's got a sponsor.

'What's that?'

Someone who's even deeper in the shit than you are. If you feel like letting go, you ring your sponsor. He'll remind you that you've had it. Have a whopper.

'Thanks.'

And guess what. His sponsor's an actor. He's six foot six and his sponsor's an actor! Anyway – when he rang me up I still thought we might be in business; that we'd been given the green light by the BBC at least.

'When was this?'

Just the other day. When you were in Mauritius with your fat man.

'Right.'

I was quite excited. 'Can I share?' he asked. Fuck, I thought. But I said OK. He was in a bad way. His sponsor had recently given him permission to have a personal relationship. His first for six months. You're not supposed to have personal relationships in recovery. But his sponsor had given him the go-ahead. Are you following this?

'Absolutely! I'm riveted!'

Good. So – he'd met this woman at a meeting. She'd be suitable, he'd thought. So he'd taken her out a couple of times and they'd got on pretty well.

'That's nice.'

Very nice. So he'd put it to her straight. 'I'd like to have a personal relationship with you,' he'd said.

'Golly. What did she say?'

She said she'd need space to think about it.

'Of course.'

She had to be careful, being in recovery too. She'd give him a decision on Thursday, she said.

'Goodness.'

Exactly. The days dragged till Thursday. He was early at the meeting. He drank six cups of coffee from a plastic mug, was rude to Mrs Moraes, confused Sir Hopkins with Paul Merson the little striker. Then she showed up. She was sorry, she said, but her sponsor had decided that she wasn't ready yet for a personal relationship.

'Oh dear. She turned him down?'

Completely. What do you think he did?

'Went on a bender?'

No. He rang his sponsor. He was in despair. He poured his heart out. He told his sponsor all about this woman. She'd been ideal, he said. Not particularly attractive, he said, indeed quite a homely type, but stuck in a failed marriage. In a nutshell, not at all exciting but suitable for someone in recovery. He raves on for half an hour about this woman, while his sponsor listens quietly. Who do you suppose she is?

'*I* don't know!'

His sponsor's wife! That took a bit of sorting out. Anyway – now he wants to share all this with me. What bad luck, eh? I meet a producer. Six foot six. Big voice. Good complexion. I think I've cracked it. He's in recovery! A producer who wants to share! Like having a publisher who wants to talk about himself. Fuck off, cunt, I said.

'So what was it? Apart from that, I mean.'

What was what?

'Your biggest flop? What was your biggest flop?'

Oh yes. *Wham Bam Thank You Mam*. That was it.

'You put the fish on first?'

Fish? What fish?

'I don't know. Seals or something. Never put the seals on first, you said.'

Seals aren't fish. Good heavens.

'Oh. So you didn't put the fish on first?'

Not on this occasion, no. That was *Nights at the Comedy*, my attempt to revive music hall. Stage thereafter as slippery as an ice-rink. *Ingénue* on next. 'Let Me Entertain You.' She skated straight into the orchestra stalls. No, my biggest flop was *Wham Bam Thank You Mam*. It opened in Brighton with a faulty revolve and without an orchestra – a consequence of my habit in those days of casting a show with the tour in mind. I always ensured that a show contained its full complement of *ingénues* – whether or not the author had made this provision – and I always saw to it that the leading man and the second lead were past their prime and with only three good legs between them. The cast on this occasion consisted of six girl dancers and four fat comedians. I'd pulled that old one out of retirement. Very fat. Very funny. Smoked a cigar. Christ. What was his name?

'I don't know!'

Don't be silly. You must do. Very funny. Used to come on dressed as a boy scout, wearing a top hat and smoking a cigar. 'Has anyone seen a very fat man dressed as a boy scout and smoking a cigar?' he used to say. 'Yes!' screamed the audience. 'Thank God for that,' he used to say. 'I thought I was lost.' That made my father rock with laughter. My father never missed a show if he was in it. You *must* remember his name.

'I *don't*. I don't know what you're talking about. Let me have another.'

No! We're running out. Look. That's all we've got left. We'll have to slow down.

'I bet you've got some more! I'm sure you've got some hidden away!'

I *haven't*.

'I'm sure you have. Let me look. Let me look in the box.'

This is *terrible*. Don't you trust me?

'I'm going to look in the box.'

Don't *do* this. God it frightens me when you do this. You *mustn't* do this. Where are you going?

'Into the kitchen. I'm going to look in the kitchen.'

No! Don't go into the kitchen.

'Stop! You're hurting!'

Sorry. But I mean it. Now – sit down and behave yourself. Christ! We were *fighting* there for a minute. You were *fighting* me for it. That's *terrible*. Don't you see?

'Sorry.'

OK. So . . .

'I'm *really* sorry. Oh God, I'm so sorry. I . . .'

That's all right. Fred Emney! That was his name. Penny? *Penny!*

'What?'

The fat comedian. My father's favourite. That was his name. I dragged him out of retirement in memory of my father. God, he was such a sweet old man. I used to have lunch with him at the Garrick.

'We could get some more!'

Christ, this is terrible. Do you know how much we've done?

'No. Don't tell me.'

Five hundred pounds' worth. Anyway. I haven't got any more cash.

'We could ring Jillypoo. She'll take a cheque, won't she? I'll give her a cheque. Please ring Jillypoo. *Please.*'

No. I'm telling you about *Wham Bam Thank You Mam.* Where was I?

'I don't know!'

I have it. Six girl dancers and four fat comedians, one of whom – Fred Emney – was obliged to change behind the revolve because he no longer had the wind to make it to the dressing-room. Plus Annie Ross and Oscar Brown Junior.

'Who's Oscar Brown Junior?'

American jazz singer. I imported him at vast expense. He was thought at the time to be the smartest thing on either side of the Atlantic. Nor did he present a problem as far as the tour was concerned. One day – without being too laddish, I think, or taking anything for granted – we agreed, Oscar and I, that he should tip his hat at Aimi MacDonald, I mine at Jacqui the Dancer.

'Jacqui the Dancer? Who's Jacqui the Dancer?'

The love of my life. Before I met you, of course. When she auditioned for *Wham Bam Thank You Mam* I thought I'd never seen anything so lovely. Then Oscar dropped a bombshell. 'What about the band?' he said.

Unaccustomed as I was to mounting musicals, I had left the band out of the equation. The love of my life was about to tour the country with eleven eligible sidemen, not least Les Condon on second trumpet and Laurie Mumford on trombone. Happily, I rose to the occasion. I arranged for the cast and management to go to Brighton, the band to Blackpool. As a consequence, Oscar Brown Junior was accompanied on the first night by Bert Leywood, my 76-year-old general manager, playing an upright piano in the pit.

And the revolve let us down. After some silly opening sketch, and to a roar of excitement from jazz buffs in the audience, Oscar was revolved on singing his heart out – 'Permit me to introduce myself/My name is Mr Kicks!' – but the revolve failed to stop and spun him off again.

Fred Emney, changing for the next skit at the back of the revolve, hopping about on one leg as he struggled to put his trousers on, was spun into view. The revolve went round thirty-two times and might still be going round had not the stage manager run on and smashed it with an axe.

The show closed immediately, but Jacqui the Dancer had been impressed by the unconquerable vigour of my love. Later, she lived with Oliver Reed for twenty years. That's by the way, however.

The point is, I dragged Fred Emney out of retirement to participate in one of my fiascos. They don't teach you that at Winchester.

'I bet they don't! I know, let's . . .'

Nor in that other place.

'What other place?'

That dreadful place in Cornwall. Where your fat man lives. What's that?

'*I* don't know!'

Of course you do. Come on. In Cornwall. By the sea. A very common place.

'Oh. Fowey? Is that it? I think it might be Fowey.'

Good. I got that right.

'What are you talking about? You got what right?'

It was an idea I had months ago for a TV development. I set it in Fowey.

'In *Fowey*? Why?'

It was just a joke. I was playing around with the idea that you might settle down there with your fat man.

'Oh, *please*! That's *gruesome*! Why ever did you do that?'

Just a joke. Anyway – they don't teach you that at Winchester. They don't, at Winchester, teach you to humiliate fine old gentlemen in public, to arrange that their farewell performance will be hopping about on one leg on a spinning revolve.

'Right!'

Let's ring up Jillypoo.

'Oh *yes* . . .'

Ideas for television shows come thick and fast. I have my development for Jonty Agnew and now an idea has dropped fully formed into my head – suitable, I think, for an episode in a snail-paced ITV country cop drama starring a crap English actor with a hobby.

Inspector Hinchcliffe, of the Devon and Cornwall police, attends a barbecue party one evening at the home of a couple in Fowey. Among the ordinary people on the lawn – cheerful tradesmen and their disappointed wives – his hostess Alison (forty-three and with her hair styled locally) seems unnecessarily ordinary even by Inspector Hinchcliffe's standards, and his enthusiasms are metal-detecting and cross-indexing the local flora.

While her fat husband, wearing a novelty apron, turns the sausages and exchanges barbecue-based *doubles entendres* with the invited tradesmen, Alison stands awkwardly at the inconspicuous margins of the party chatting inexpertly with other abandoned wives. Some of the wives, empowered by years of neglect, drink too much and flirt rather gauchely with one another's husbands, but Alison hasn't even the residual confidence for that. She seems to be utterly defeated, the spirit squeezed out of her by the suburban certainties exemplified by her smug and dominating husband.

What an *unlived* existence the poor woman must have had, the Inspector thinks to himself, as later that night he goes over the events of the barbecue party in his mind. She hadn't even come alive when, out of courtesy, he'd asked her what plans, if any, she had for the education of her two quite unattractive children, Toby, ten, and Kate, eight. (Inspector Hinchcliffe doesn't particularly like children. His own wife is confined, for no very obvious dramatic reason, to a wheelchair.)

The next morning Alison's dead body is found at the bottom of a Cornish cliff. Alison, the Inspector discovers, had been in the habit of taking solitary early morning walks, and the assumption is that she lost her footing. Death by accident is the coroner's verdict, but the Inspector is troubled by some of the evidence – not least a photograph with some writing on the back that Alison was clutching tightly in her hand at the time of her fall.

The picture is of a laughing girl of fourteen or so, wearing braces on her teeth and dressed in a school uniform, and behind her stands a muscular man in his early thirties. The message on the back reads: 'Was there ever such a day, Marion, was there ever such a day?'

The Inspector recognizes the girl as Alison, so why does the message refer to Marion? Who is the man (not Alison's fat and domineering husband, clearly), and why did Alison cherish this photograph thirty years after it was taken? The Inspector decides now, and in his own time, to unravel Alison's past.

What he gradually discovers about this ordinary woman, met at a humdrum barbecue party on a Cornish lawn, quite surprises him. Tracing her life backwards, he learns that she was the product of an unhappy marriage between a weak south London architect and his drunken, sadistic wife. It was the wife's practice, when she had guests to dinner, to summon Alison, aged nine, into her presence, order her to rehearse her misdemeanours and then, in front of the guests, to slap her naked bottom and send her crying back to bed.

Frightened and alone in her little upstairs room, Alison –certain that she must deserve this punishment – would repeat over and over again to herself: 'I didn't mean to! I'm so sorry! I really didn't mean to!' – before crying herself to sleep.

When Alison was eleven there was some scandal at her local convent – later hushed up – possibly involving a sudden terrified attack on a bullying older girl with a sharpened comb. At thirteen, and unable any longer to put up with her parents' endless drunken brawling, Alison ran away from home and moved in with her schoolfriend Simon.

Thereafter, she was brought up by Simon's parents – Jake, a local rough diamond with fists like hams and a taste for quoting Shakespeare, and by Jake's wife, Margaret, a patient woman who worked for the council and was the household's only source of income.

Jake helped Alison with her homework, quoted Shakespeare, taught her to play tennis and took her for long walks on Wimbledon Common. When she was fourteen, confusing him perhaps with the strong father she'd never had, Alison fell in love with Jake – one day playing truant from school and, dressed in her convent uniform, seducing him under the Jack and Jill windmills on the Sussex Downs. With Margaret's resigned approval Alison moved into Jake's bedroom and Margaret moved to another part of the house.

Alison was happy now, or so it seemed, but when she was seventeen the laughing, seemingly joyful schoolgirl first demonstrated an unusual capacity for deception. Having told Jake that she had found employment in a wine bar, she signed up with an escort agency in the West End. For the next eight years Jake, Alison and Margaret managed, by avoiding awkward questions, to live in harmony.

Alison became ever more accomplished in the habits of conceal-ment, and Jake and Margaret turned a blind eye to this extra source of household income, to Alison's increasingly knowing wardrobe, to her trips around the world and to the Mitsubishi Shogun parked outside their Balham villa.

Alison never cried herself to sleep again. She had let her parents down (why else had they punished her?), but she would be loved for ever by Jake for the money she was bringing in and for the expen-sive, thoughtful presents that she always brought back for him from her trips around the world. She had redeemed herself at last and would never be punished again.

Then, when she was twenty-four, two other older men became enchanted by her mysterious composure, her steady gaze, her ability not to be disturbed by the most gauche middle-aged suggestion: John, a wealthy software man from Fowey – met at the escort agency – and Martin, a somewhat raddled television journalist, similarly encountered.

To broaden her cultural horizons Martin took her on foreign shoots, introduced her to colleagues at the Groucho Club, casually displayed memorabilia concerning celebrated former lovers (some of whom Alison had heard of), plied her with hallucinatory drugs and gave her books to read. It would not have occurred to Martin that Alison would ever prefer a less interesting man than him.

When she was thirty, and suddenly craving an ordinary life, Alison arranged one day for Jake to have a medical check-up early on a cold November morning and, while he was strapped to a clinic's table with a laboratory technician's finger up his arse, she packed their joint possessions into her Mitsubishi Shogun and drove to Cornwall where she moved in with her simple software salesman.

Jake, the bookish, soft-centred local action man, and Martin, the semi-educated documentary-maker, were left to find comfort in remembered verses. Jake startled other mourners in a local cemetery by wearing an autumnal face and quoting Shakespeare ('Let's talk of graves, of worms and epitaphs/Make dust our paper and with rainy eyes/Write sorrow on the bosom of the earth'), while Martin recited Larkin in the morning ('Can denial duck and run/Stay out of sight and double round/Leap from the sun with mask and brand/And murder and not understand?') and, in the early evening, sought consolation by copying chunks of Canetti on to the backs of tear-stained envelopes (envelopes which, ten years later, are discovered by Inspector Hinchcliffe), including this from *The Human Province* and from which, had Martin been wiser, he might have learnt something before it was too late:

> The true Don Quixote, an unsurpassable fool, would be one to wage the struggle against a woman's desires with words, with *sheer* words. She feels this desire for others. The fool, who once loved her and cannot face the way she is now, decides to fight with words. What he wants to give her flows into the words he finds for her. Without words, he could have accomplished everything.

Soon enough, and greatly inflated by the words of others, Jake and Martin each sought to subdue his grief by more ambitious literary activity – Jake on lined leaves torn from a school exercise book embarking on a regretful fiction and Martin almost completing a bitter-sweet memoir. Ten years later their abandoned efforts fall into the hands of Inspector Hinchcliffe, providing him with source material when piecing together Alison's life.

In my episode of a crap ITV country cop show, the Inspector will never discover whether Alison's death was indeed an accident, but he will learn this: never assume that the dull woman encountered at a provincial barbecue party doesn't have secrets up her sleeve.

I'm quite pleased with this and will discuss it with Pete the Schnoz when next he rings.

★

Pete the Schnoz should by now have made his second phone call from Bangkok. It's a problem of construction, really. Playing around with time, as I am, trying to arrange the past, present and future into an intelligible pattern, causes organizational difficulties.

Never mind. Pete the Schnoz rings now. He's forgotten our last conversation, so I take it he's been at the Rohypnol again.

'Pharmacies in Bangkok,' he says, 'are like English driving ranges. They have buckets at the entrance and . . .'

'You told me that,' I say.

This surprises him. 'Really? When?'

'When you called before.'

'I called before? I don't remember that.'

'Well, you did. You'd just bought a Polaroid camera to secure a visual record of your next adventure. What happened?'

What didn't happen. According to Pete the Schnoz, he and Cathy doubled the Rohypnol dose and woke up the next morning, un-handcuffed this time and in their own hotel room but surrounded by photographic evidence suggesting that they had at some point in the evening persuaded half the artistes in Bangkok's red-light district to party with them in their suite.

'The Polaroids are astonishing,' says Pete the Schnoz. 'Apart from me and Cathy – neither of us at our most pukka – the room is strewn with transvestites, sailors, cabaret acrobats, tattooists, triple-jointed escapologists and tiny oriental masseuses who, by a lifetime of yogic disciplines, are able, the Polaroids suggest, to introduce three-quarters of their bodyweight into their own genital areas.

'Alas, we don't remember any of it. We've got the answer, however. We've now acquired a video camera and we'll rig it up tonight. That should do the trick.'

After Pete the Schnoz has rung off I decide that I shouldn't sample my own supply of Rohypnol since I don't want my memory erased just as I'm about to start my memoirs. I ought to hide them, I suppose, but the only way to ensure that I'll forget the hiding place is to take a Rohypnol first, which is exactly the opposite, of course, of what I want to do. And then I think, what the hell, and I take one anyway.

And later I realize that I still haven't mentioned the *Root* special to Pete the Schnoz. Nor did I mention my idea for a crap ITV country cop drama with a duff English actor playing a Police Inspector with a hobby. Never mind. Pete the Schnoz will ring again.

There are four more calls, in the sequence of six, still to come.

The Editor of the *Evening Standard* magazine wants me to interview the writer Robin Cook, who in the sixties had some success apparently with his novel *The Crust on Its Uppers*. Now his autobiography, *The Hidden Files*, is to be published.

'Cook went to Eton,' the Editor explains, 'and in the sixties led quite a shady existence – dabbling in deception, pornography and so forth. It might be amusing, I think, to bring two writers together with equally questionable pasts.'

That's OK. I don't object to his suggestion that I have a questionable past – not something that would have occurred to me but an interpretation worth looking at when I start my memoirs. I accept the commission and am told that *The Hidden Files* will be biked round later in the day. By the time the book arrives, however, I have decided not to read it, since a theory about Cook – based on the rackety early CV (Eton drop-out, class traitor, counter hand in a porno bookshop, underworld *habitué*) – is already forming in my mind and I don't want it to be refuted by anything in his memoirs.

By the evening I've got Mr Cook well summed up; I could, frankly, do the interview without him. That said, I will keep our rendezvous at the Coach And Horses, Soho (where he insists we meet), but I intend to supply not just the questions but the answers too. I'll emerge with credit from the interview by pointing out to Cook that rebels like him are just a nuisance; are, sooner or later, parasitical on decent people who have married and taken out insurance, have made arrangements for the future and have a shed with a motor- mower in it. I'll explain to Cook that the trail of havoc rebels leave behind – bewildered wives, bruised tradesmen – can never be justified by the 'work'.

And if he quotes Nietzsche or Browning at me, counters with sentimental stuff about life at the dangerous edge of things being the only one worth living – or, still more reprehensibly, that without the 'life' the 'work' would somehow not be possible – I'll suggest that a writer's place is at his desk, not splashing his personality around in Soho pubs.

THURSDAY 11.56 p.m.

Christ. I thought we'd never get rid of her.

'She's brilliant, Jillypoo.'

She does go on, though. Still – it's a good deal. We're all right now.

'Me first! *Please*! Let me be first!'

OK. Here. Guess what.

'What?'

Saffy is thinking of going on the game.

'*Never!* When did she tell you that?'

When we went out with her and Pratley. The night before you went to Mauritius with your fat man. She thinks it will release her.

'She's cuckoo, Saffy.'

I don't know. She's right in a way. It helps if you've been paid. It means you're acting. It's not really *you* doing these things. When I was a producer I could never understand why actresses got so upset if you didn't pay them. But they had a point. We'd all get upset if we'd made thundering fools of ourselves six nights a week and twice on Saturdays and then, at the end of it, we'd not been paid.

'Can I have another?'

What must have the force of truth must not be true. Nietzsche.

'Really?'

Really. He meant, of course, that tarts shouldn't enjoy themselves.

'Yeah?'

No. He was making the related point, I think, that the actor playing Romeo will give a less effective performance if he happens to be in love with the actress playing Juliet. He must *act* the emotion. This is certainly the case in my experience.

'You've never been an actor!'

No. But I've been on the game.

'*What! When?* You haven't been on the game!'

I have. I've done hundreds of tricks. Well – one.

'*When?* I want to know when. Tell me when.'

When you were in Mauritius with your fat man. I kicked Barclay the Banker round the room for Tracey, your beloved.

'What! You said you *wouldn't*! I told you *not* to!'

I know. I defied you. How about that?

'I can't *believe* this! Why? *Why* did you?'

Tracey kept pressing me, so in the end I agreed. It was very odd. I certainly couldn't have done it as me. I did it as Tony the Drug Fiend. He wanted to taste the low-life, Barclay the Banker. He wanted to take hard drugs and be kicked from pillar to post by a sleaze in a raincoat. What could be easier than that? I thought. But I was useless. I couldn't act the low-life in the least. I offered him a glass of sherry and discussed the cricket. 'What about the big lad, Hick?' I said. 'Has he come to terms at last with the test match atmosphere?' I wanted him to like me, do you see? Not what he was paying for at all. I dare say I've lost him for Tracey as a client.

'You're pulling my leg. I *know* you are.'

Not in the least. The next day he went to the bank as usual – crisp white shirt, spruce and dapper, 'The correspondence with Singapore, Miss Casparry, if you'd be so good' – and opened the

Evening Standard. There's a picture of me interviewing the thriller writer Robin Cook. The penny drops. He's been roped and left squealing like a pig by Henry Root no less. Bit of a shock. He may have gone mad.

'This is terrible. Tell me you're joking.'

I'm serious. What's wrong with it?

'It's in *very* bad taste. It's appalling.'

You were doing the same. You were away in Mauritius doing a trick.

'That's *different*.'

I don't see why.

'It just *is*. Tell me you're joking.'

I'm joking. Of course I didn't do it. I turned it down. I told Tracey that you wouldn't let me.

'Phew! I really believed you for a minute. That was *really* bad! Tell me what else you didn't do when I was away. Did you crack those hidden things?'

Hidden things? What hidden things?

'All that stuff you discovered in your notebook. After you'd taken Rohypnol. Stuff you couldn't understand. Stuff in code, you said. About Helmut Newton and the banker's daughter. Stuff about Sarah finding the Polaroids. It sounded good, that. Did you discover what it meant?'

I did eventually. I cracked it.

'Tell me what it meant.'

Later. I'll tell you later.

'OK. Tell me something else, then. Something for your memoirs.'

Right. I'll tell you about the time I attempted to defraud Sir Donald Albery. J. P. Donleavy's *Fairy Tales of New York* had just opened at the Comedy and . . .

'Can I have another?'

Look. I'm telling you an anecdote here. You said you wanted to hear an anecdote.

'I've changed my mind.'

Oh. I know.

'What?'

I wanted to ask you something. Was it true about the football boots?

'Football boots? What football boots?'

When you were a little girl. You wanted to play football with Simon and his friends. But they wouldn't let you. You thought it might be because you didn't have proper football boots. So you went and bought a pair. Is that true?

'Yes. What's wrong with that?'

Nothing. It's adorable.

'What do you mean, adorable? It was sensible. I saved up for weeks. I wanted to play.'

And did they let you?

'Yes. Eventually. I was very good.'

I bet you were. I think I'm going to cry.

'Don't do that! Tell me something else. Tell me why I'm better than Melanie. Tell me again.'

Well – she'd deny stuff. She'd get doubts and say that what she'd done hadn't really been her. Or she'd blame the drugs. You never do that. You never have doubts.

'Why should I? I don't do things I'll regret later. I only do what I want to do.'

Even on this?

'Specially on this!'

You never feel you've gone too far? Even with Tracey?

'*Never!*'

Tell me what she makes you do. Tell me something you haven't told me before.

'OK. One time she blindfolded me in a taxi. I didn't know where she was taking me. Later I discovered it was this smart flat in Knightsbridge. The room was full of strangers.'

Christ. Go on.

'She made me stand in the middle of the room. Then I was slowly undressed. I stood there naked. I couldn't see anything, but I could feel these hands touching me. I didn't know who they were.'

Did you like it?

'Of course I did.'

You were excited?

'Jesus yes! I'm excited now, telling you.'

What then? What happened then?

'Will you punish me if I tell you?'

Of course I will. If it's bad. If it's really bad.

'It is bad. What will you do to me? Tell me. Tell me now.'

Not yet. Later. After you've had another. Here. I'll hold it . . .

I have given an ambitious Rohypnol-inspired twist to my episode of a crap ITV country cop drama involving a police inspector with a hobby and the death under a Cornish cliff of Alison, the defeated wife of a software salesman. Ambitious, because it obliges me to write an explicit scene, and one, furthermore, featuring the seduction of a schoolgirl.

Inspector Hinchcliffe, of the Devon and Cornwall Police, will discover that after Alison ran off with John, her ignorant computer man, Martin, the raddled television journalist who had supposed she loved him, and Jake, the ageing south London action man who had brought her up, met in a wine bar and, united in grief, became friends.

In a telling scene Jake admits with customary gruffness (an acquired abrasiveness which only fitfully hides his innate decency and shyness) that he too is writing a book about Alison. Would Martin read it and offer his advice? Martin agrees, thereafter quite forgetting the incident until, some days later, he is interrupted while deep in composition of his memoirs by the arrival of a package in the post.

It turns out to be Jake's manuscript – just a few pages handwritten in large capital letters on paper torn from an exercise book. Thinking it best to discharge this irritating duty quickly – and worried already about how to report honestly to Jake without hurting his feelings – Martin starts to read.

My son and some schoolfriends were standing round a skinny kid with new shorts and football boots.

'Hey, Dad, this is Alison. She's on our side, OK?'

The new kid half smiled, revealing heavy braces on her upper and lower teeth. Her hair was cut in a bob and she wore a green Coq Sportif football shirt. Her legs were milk white.

'Hullo, Mr Sutherland. I'm Simon's friend. He said I couldn't play because I didn't have proper boots. So I went out and bought some! Look! Aren't they brilliant? Can I play now? *Please* can I play?'

Still that shy half-smile, looking up at me with longing in her large hazel-green eyes. It would be difficult to turn her away. I looked questioningly at Simon.

'She'll be OK, Dad. She really wants to play.'

Drawing Simon aside, I pointed out that the Balham bunch looked wired.

'It's OK, Dad. We'll look after her.'

From that moment on, there was always a man to look after Alison.

The game commenced, half an hour each way. Our new kid moved out to the right wing. Her white legs and brand-new boots clashing with the home boys' jeans and trainers.

Running up and down the touchline, Alison at last gave the ball a mighty stiff-legged kick, followed by peals of happy laughter. The joy of that laughter was infectious, and the Balham bad boys resisted kicking her till late in the second half.

My son was first into battle as the recriminations followed.

Mayhem for three or four minutes until the elders were able to break it up. Above the kicking, swearing youths I heard Alison's joyful laughter.

Later that sunny afternoon Simon explained that Alison lived just down the road. She was eleven. Two years later she ran away in the middle of the night and came to live with us.

And within a year of that day Alison and I lay down side by side in a field under the shadows of the Jack and Jill Windmills on the South Downs.

All afternoon we had sunbathed on Brighton beach. Alison, who was playing truant, was wearing her school uniform. She had removed her wedge cork-soled shoes, her green school stockings and her white blouse. We lay together and she moved nearer to me. Her white arm brushed occasionally against mine.

'Let's go up to the Downs, Jake,' said Alison quietly.

'Yeah, OK, it will be nice up there now.'

It was approaching dusk as we drove into The Windmill car park. We climbed a stile and walked hand in hand across a field. We were the only people there. We were the only people in the world.

We sat down under the cover of a huge oak tree. It felt hotter here than on the beach. We both knew why we were here.

'I won't hurt you. Ally. I promise.'

'I know that, Jake.'

'Just tell me to stop if it hurts.'

'OK.'

Alison presses her closed lips to mine. I push my mouth hard on to hers. The steely taste of her braces explodes in my brain. I run my hand up and down the inside of her skinny white thighs.

'Do it now, Jake. Do it now, please.'

'We'll do it slowly, OK?'

Rolling over between Alison' s legs, I reach down and press slowly into her. Her whole body quivers and a moan bursts from her lips. Her hands reach up and press against my shoulders.

'I can't, Jake! I can't! It's too . . .'

I take Alison's hands from my shoulders and pin them at her side. Her hands struggle free and clasp themselves round my neck – pulling me down, pulling me in.

Her face is invisible in the dusk and her mouth finds mine. Her braces crush my lips. I hold my breath and then explode inside her. Alison doesn't move. An eternity goes by, then a sigh. Followed by a laugh.

'What, Ally?'

'It feels good, Jake. I want to sit in the car and feel it all the way home.'

We look around in the darkness and find her green school knickers. She pulls them on, sighing and giggling.

'Is this how it will always be, Jake?'

'Yes, Ally. This is how it will always be.'

We walk slowly back up the field to the car park. The twin windmills are silhouetted against the night sky. Hand in hand we turn and look back over the South Downs. The headlights of the cars far below breaking the darkness.

I speak softly. 'Was there ever such a day, Marion? Was there ever such a day?'

'Who's Marion, Jake? Why Marion? Who is she?' This in a quiet, puzzled voice.

I pull her to me and hug her tightly. Leaning down, I kiss her forehead, her nose, her eyes. She is crying softly and the salty taste of her tears is on my lips. I can still taste those tears.

'Don't worry, Ally. It was just someone saying it better than I ever could.'

'I love you, Jake.'

'I think I love you, Ally.'

We make our way back over the stile and into the car park. The drive back to London is made in complete silence. Getting out of the car in Hendrick Avenue, her first words since Brighton.

'I'm so happy, Jake. Will I always be this happy?'

The voice is lower, satisfied – a woman's voice. We left the girl under the shadows of the Windmills. Then that joyful laugher. Now I can't remember it. Alison took her laughter with her.

Reading these few artless pages, Martin is plunged into some sort of personal catastrophe. In a moment of rare self-knowledge, he understands that, wherever Alison now is, she will carry with her no memory of him to compare with this one; further, and more seriously, that his own endlessly worked over and self-dramatizing account of his days with her is oddly less effective than the unembarrassed simplicity of Jake's handwritten pages. In disgust Martin abandons his manuscript and hides it away in a drawer – from where, ten years later, and after Alison's apparently accidental death under a Cornish cliff, it is recovered by Inspector Hinchcliffe. Thereafter, Martin reclusively exhausts his dwindling stock of literary ambitions by the endless copying out of passages from *The Human Province* on to whatever scraps of paper come to hand: unpaid bills, circulars from the Cartoon Trust, requests for funding from Cambridge University, mailshots from the art gallery down the road.

'Some people,' he gloatingly copies, 'can only love with a strong feeling of guilt. Their passion ignites on whatever they are ashamed of; it becomes their haven, like God for believers after they have sinned. They want to be afraid and they love a person only if their fear of him never dies. When he stops reproaching them and does not punish them for anything, when they have won him over to such an extent that he is satisfied with them, their love dies and everything ends.'

Ten years later Inspector Hinchcliffe discovers this in Martin's flat, scribbled on the back of a final demand from British Gas. Not being a particularly well-read man he fails to recognize its source, but he does wonder whether it explains Alison's death at the bottom of a Cornish cliff. Had John, her fat software salesman, stopped reproaching her? Had he finally failed her as a father? Had everything ended for her just before that last solitary walk, clutching the photograph of herself, aged fourteen, and Jake – the only man, perhaps, by whom she wished to be punished always? 'Was there ever such a day, Marion, was there ever such a day?' For Inspector Hinchcliffe the case is closed.

I'm quite pleased with this – not least with my Rohypnol-aided attempt to write in the style of a sentimental south London tearaway. I look forward to discussing it with Pete the Schnoz. He'll be impressed, I think.

Waiting for the Publisher to return to our table, I decide now to break the first rule of successful banking, which is never to meet the manager. If you're just a blip on a computer screen you might be up to anything, but if the manager meets you he can see you've had it.

Or might he not? Brooding now about madness in general, it strikes me that most of the people I know are a little odd. They're not yet carrying all their possessions in a Co-op shopping-bag, growling at strangers in the street or trumpeting generalized rage and pain on top of buses, but they're not in any obvious sense quite all there.

Jillypoo believes that the Masons are persecuting her and she accordingly sits at her front window round the clock with a night-sighted air rifle across her knees. Tankybums, with whom I used to shrimp in Broadstairs in the summer holidays and who still lives with his 96-year-old mother in the country, believes that whenever Frank Sinatra visits England he always calls on Tankybums in Sittingbourne. And my friend Scott the Screenwriter won't take books out of the library because he fears he may catch someone else's germs.

All certifiable, I'd have thought, yet each of them seems to be better at the nuts and bolts of living – paying the community charge and so forth – than I am or have ever been. Perhaps it's me who's got it wrong, not them.

Equally, in a world so out of kilter that the claims of a black man to be the King of Spain are taken seriously – further, one in which the probity of someone as obviously mad as Black Simone is weighed carefully by a magistrate and judged thereafter to be superior to mine – might I not be granted an overdraft by the Midland Bank plc in order that I might secure the King's release?

Accordingly, I drop in at the Midland Bank, Sloane Square, to see the manager, Mr Zeberdee, whom I've never met. Mindful that the way to impress bankers is to be brief, confident and to the point, I am determined not to say too much, not to embarrass Mr Zeberdee with details that are no concern of his. I judge that there are certain things which young Mr Zeberdee, like the Publisher, would as soon not know – the stuff, for instance, about visiting the *Folies Bergère* at the age of thirteen and seeing women thereafter as performers only; about my affair with Law, now a judge; and about Harry A, the Secretary in his day of the MCC.

These are precisely the sort of details I'd rather hear from a total stranger than his views on money management, but I judge that bankers are different in this regard. Equally, and however interested I might be in his answers, I must on no account ask Mr Zeberdee the only sort of questions which you or I would think worth putting. Is he happy? Does he slump somewhat in the early afternoon? Has it hit him yet that soon enough we'll all be dead? What hopes does he hold out for himself and Mrs Zeberdee?

Against this, of course, is the fact that the Midland, in a radical departure from former policy, is now 'the Listening Bank', keen to finesse you into thinking that they yearn for a *personal* relationship with their customers. I decide, therefore, to take the middle way – neither embarrassing young Mr Zeberdee by telling him too much, nor by saying too little, suggesting that I'm unimpressed by the bank's new slogan. I tell him, briefly, that I'm a writer; that I'm about to start work on my memoirs, *From Winchester to This*.

'The past and the present side by side,' I say. 'How, in spite of one's background – Sunningdale. Winchester, the Navy, Cambridge – one can still end up in the shit.'

Mr Zeberdee seems interested; he doesn't draw back, look at me warily or ask me if I have a house. He is the bank's slogan personified. He is looking at me expectantly, as if he wants me to continue – but I must be careful here. Bankers aren't necessarily stupid. Young Mr Zeberdee may be giving me enough rope to hang myself. I mustn't tell him too much. He maintains this unnerving silence, though, so I carry on – pointing out that I have other stuff in the pipeline too. Central television, I say, having got over the débâcle of *Root Into Europe*, have just commissioned a *Root* special, which I intend to write with Pete the Schnoz.

'Perhaps you know the Schnoz's work?' I say.

'Alas, I don't,' says Mr Zeberdee.

'Nor do I. But I hear only the best reports of it. The *Root* special, with the Schnoz at the helm, will be a great improvement.'

And then, judging that Mr Zeberdee isn't yet sufficiently impressed by my schedule, I tell him about my proposed contribution to the BBC2 series *My Secret Life*. I shall be shown living in fear, I say, in case my friends at Happy's crack-house, having discovered that I work secretly for the *Independent* and dine from time to time at Boodles, may think less of me.

'I shall pitch it shortly to my new friend Jonty Agnew,' I say. 'He's six foot six with a loud voice, so I have every hope that he'll be able to set it up. Rather good, don't you think?'

Mr Zeberdee still seems happiest as the personification of the bank's new slogan, so, fearful that any minute now I'll show my anxiety by saying too much – by speaking of Harry A and the high court judge, of dark sides and little Katharine Hamnett skirts and long nights of appetite and shame – I come swiftly to the point, explaining that I'd been in court two days ago attempting to spring the rightful King of Spain.

'And what a peculiar business that was,' I say. 'At one point, and in the witness box, Black Simone said: "I'm sixty–forty he's the fucking King, m'lud." You'd have laughed if you'd been there, Mr Zeberdee. Here's the point, however: the magistrate will only bail the King into my safe keeping if I can show that I'm good for £5,000.'

Mr Zeberdee continues to stare at me expectantly, so, judging that I haven't told him enough yet about my expertise at money management – indeed, I haven't told him anything – I'm about to describe my attempt to defraud Sir Donald Albery in 1961, when at last he speaks.

'The past and the present side by side?' he says.

'I'm sorry?'

'Your memoirs.' Mr Zeberdee glances at some notes he seems to have scratched in his banker's journal. *'From Winchester to This*. How the past shapes the future, is that it?'

'Indeed. And vice versa. Present experience alters one's perception of the past. And, of course, of the future, too.'

Mr Zeberdee looks puzzled. 'The future? I'm not sure if I follow you.'

'In a sense the future's closed. Statements about the future are true or false *now*. My memoirs all take place in the course of a long and – to excuse the embarrassment of unasked-for personal disclosures – crack-fuelled conversation with Penny, my beloved. This occurs *after* she gets back from her trip to Mauritius with her fat man.'

'Which is in the future.'

'*Now* it is. But in my memoirs it will be in the past. But not so far in the past as this conversation we're having now. In my memoirs it will be possible, if I judge it helpful, to refer back to this meeting during the conversation with Penny, my beloved.'

Mr Zeberdee seems to understand. 'So – everything's been

decided,' he says. 'Is that it? By the time the reader experiences this conversation it will be in the past?'

'Precisely. But I can't help that. I couldn't write about you at all unless you were, in a sense, already over. Finished. Discarded. Done with. Consigned, as far as the reader is concerned, to some ghostly limbo for unimportant characters in someone else's memoirs.'

'Fascinating,' says Mr Zeberdee. 'And this fat man . . .'

'Fat man? What fat man?'

Once again, Mr Zeberdee consults his notes. 'The fat man from Cornwall who plans to take Penny, your beloved, to Mauritius. He's some sort of presiding villain, is he?'

That takes me by surprise. I have never thought of Penny's fat man as any sort of villain. A presiding buffoon, if anything.

'Hardly,' I say. 'The man's in software. He attends software conferences with his name pinned to his lapel. At home he wears a yachting cap, I imagine, and would be at ease at a barbecue on a Cornish lawn. Abroad he carries a camcorder and tourist literature to do with historical remains. You'll know the type.'

'I'm not sure if I . . .'

'I'll tell you who he is. I have a friend called Debbie Mason. She runs Kudos – a television production company – and is in most respects the perfect woman. That said, her private life is, at the moment, somewhat at sixes and sevens. She finds herself unable to choose between two of her many admirers: Roberto, her live-in Italian boy, and Mark Lawrenson, Liverpool's one-time central defender. Personally I hope she chooses her Italian boy, since I find that the more erotic scenario, but my preferences, I suppose, are neither here nor there.

'Be that as it may, I lunched with Miss Mason recently and, while I was waiting for her at quite an unpleasant brasserie, I couldn't help noticing how frightful all the other lunchers looked: office personnel, for the most part, who had taken their jackets off and were, for all I could tell, trying to sell each other software. When Miss

Mason arrived I naturally asked her who these people were.

' "Members of the general public," she said.

'That hadn't occurred to me, I must admit – but she was right, of course. However, when I pointed out to Miss Mason that they might, on closer acquaintance, turn out to be less frightful than they looked, she surprised me by saying that, on the contrary, they'd be even worse.

' "Is it your opinion, then," I said, "that there are, say, just a hundred people in the whole of London who are worth knowing?"

' "Certainly," she said.

' "And that these hundred people sooner or later get to know each other?"

' "Precisely," she said. "The others are mere members of the general public. They watch *Inspector Morse*, say 'No peace for the wicked' and sell each other software."

'A somewhat élitist judgement, Mr Zeberdee, but that, in any case, is who my baby's fat man is. He's a member of the general public – the sort of man whom you see in a brasserie with his jacket off when you're waiting for Debbie Mason to arrive.'

Mr Zeberdee seems to understand. 'Of course, of course,' he says. 'I take your point. So he's no sort of threat, then? I'm thinking of narrative complexity here.'

It's an interesting idea and, to be fair to Mr Zeberdee, one that I have never considered. I think about it now, shortly concluding that it won't work. By this point in my memoirs my baby's contempt for her fat man will be too well established for the reader to swallow this device.

'It wouldn't be credible,' I say.

'Does that matter?' says Mr Zeberdee. 'As we've already decided, you can, for narrative purposes, say anything you like. You can, if you wish, perform conjuring tricks with future reality. You can cheat.'

Delighted though as I am with Mr Zeberdee's 'We've decided' (this construction establishing that my memoirs are now a joint venture with the Listening Bank), I'm a little upset by his cheating accusation.

'If you want to put it like that,' I say. 'But bear this in mind: the reader can "cheat" as easily as the narrator. The reader could skip now to the last page to see how it ends. And here, obviously, he or she has the advantage over me. *I* don't know how it ends.'

Mr Zeberdee seems surprised, sceptical, even. 'You *don't*?'

'Not *now* I don't. Not at this moment, sitting here in your office. We're talking about things that haven't happened yet. I've had various ideas, of course. One is to confuse Penny increasingly with Melanie, from whom she inherited the role. Another is to take my cue from Miss Vicky.'

'Miss Vicky?'

'My hairdresser. She advised me to be kinder to Pratley.'

'And Pratley?'

'Pratley is everyone I've been trying to shake off for twenty years. Resentful old men who were someone once but are now out of it and lonely, who ring at the wrong time, who ring with a Goon impression when you're staring at the phone willing it to be your dealer on the line. Miss Vicky advised me to be kinder to Pratley since he might be the only person speaking to me soon. I thought that that might be how it ends. After my baby dumps me...'

'Does she dump you?'

'I can't know *that* yet. But when she dumps me – if she dumps me – I was going to wait with ever-diminishing hope for the telephone to ring. But my baby doesn't call. No one calls. Not even Pratley. So, suddenly feeling very frightened, I ring up Pratley. But Pratley won't speak to me. Affecting, right?'

'Well...'

'But now I've had another idea. I might introduce Michelle.'

'Michelle?'

'A common-law wife from hell. Michelle may take me lower than I'd ever imagined possible.'

'Oh dear...'

'Oh dear indeed. Put it this way, Mr Zeberdee. We've all been *ordinarily* low, isn't that so? We've all been in thrall to a common girl in a riot skirt and bondage boots...'

'Well...'

'A really dirty girl who is at once insatiable and contemptuous, who doesn't wear knickers...'

'I'm not sure if...'

'... and when she bends over her tiny skirt rides up her soft milky thighs and...'

'I think perhaps...'

'... you can see *everything*. And in order to keep her there, this dirty girl who is flesh and heat and shameful abandonment, because you are terrified of the moment when she may never bend over again and show you everything, you...'

'Well...'

'... buy a whole *ounce* of cocaine, and you do the whole lot at a sitting, right? And we all know what that's like. We all know what it's like to lie in bed with our brains reeling and our hearts pounding and outside the fucking birds are beginning to sing and in two hours' time we've got to be in a meeting with our accountant in WC fucking 1. I mean, we've all been there, right?'

'Well, speaking for myself...'

'And it's frightening, very frightening indeed, but we know, even at its worst – even while we lie in bed crushed by the weight of our own weakness and while the fucking birds sing outside – we know that if we keep calm, if we don't panic, we will eventually come down again, back to normality, back to sanity, we'll be OK. Am I right, Mr Zeberdee? You'll have overdone it a few times, been crushed by the weight of your own weakness.'

'Well, as I say...'

'But Michelle will take me somewhere else entirely. A place from which there's no return. I'll lie there staring upwards while the birds sing in the street and there'll be no forgiveness this time. This time I'll know I've had it.'

'Don't you think, perhaps . . .'

'Listen, Mr Zeberdee. Michelle will make me crazy. Under her spell I'll do mad things in the middle of the night. I'll do things at 4 a.m. that would seem foolhardy to Pete the Schnoz or Will Self.'

'I'm sure that if . . .'

'Wishing to buy a new windproof lighter – as you'll know, Mr Zeberdee, when smoking cocaine one uses up a lot of windproof lighters – it will seem sensible to run round the Royal Borough of Kensington and Chelsea at 4 a.m. looking for an all-night tobacconist. Michelle is seriously dangerous. That's the point of her.'

'You're saying, are you, that she's turned her back on conventional morality?'

'Michelle has turned her back on *un*conventional morality. Michelle would skin you alive for a rock. At the sight of her street dealers stiffen with alarm and back away. They roll their eyes, take you to one side and advise you not to see her. "She's bad news, my man. You shouldn't be mixin' with types like her." '

Mr Zeberdee nods sympathetically. 'You should heed the advice of these gentlemen, perhaps.'

'Don't worry. I haven't met her yet. I may never meet her. She's the fiancée of my close friend Andy From The Sixties. He did eight years for supplying Princess Margaret's friends. He may introduce us.'

'You and Princess Margaret?'

'Oh for Christ's sake! No no no. I've known Princess Margaret for longer than I've known Andy From The Sixties – though I haven't seen her, I must admit, since we both lunched some years ago at the Bishop of Southwark's Tooting Palace. The Bishop drank too much, told a joke in poor taste and laughed so much himself that he fell backwards off his chair.

'He was a very nice man, as it happens, whom I'd met when he was the Vicar of the University Church, Cambridge. When my father died I was woken at seven in the morning by the Bishop of Southwark standing over my bed in a purple dress. It's no joke to be woken at 7 a.m. by a man in a dress telling you that your father's died – even when cash, share certificates and shipping-lines are in the offing.

'As for Princess Margaret, I fell out with her shortly after the lunch at Tooting Palace. She had recently taken up with a photographer who, some years earlier, had designed the sets for a musical. A very vulgar evening, as I recall. Where was I?'

Mr Zeberdee, still the personification of the bank's slogan, tells me that I have just mentioned Michelle and my possible introduction to her by her fiancé Andy From The Sixties.

'Thank you. Michelle may be the *future* future. When my baby dumps me – if she dumps me – Michelle may inherit the little Katharine Hamnett skirt and the inverted commas. Michelle may arrive a little late on Thursdays, wearing her legs and ready to perform. The past bearing down on the present, do you see? A suggestion that we never learn. It might end with me telling it all to her. I don't know yet.'

Mr Zeberdee is looking rather troubled. 'Are you sure this hasn't already happened?' he asks.

I hasten to reassure him. 'How could it have? However, if you're worried about my overdraft . . .'

Mr Zeberdee stiffens, like a dozing sentry suddenly alerted by a bugle. He consults his banker's journal.

'An overdraft?' he says. 'What overdraft? I see nothing here about an overdraft.'

'The small overdraft I hope you're going to give me. However, let's not go into that at the moment. My general point, *vis-à-vis* my memoirs, is this: I don't, sitting here now, know which of the possible endings I'll choose.'

Mr Zeberdee is still looking very troubled, though whether he's concerned about my overdraft or the effectiveness of my alternative endings it's impossible to tell. At last he speaks.

'It seems to me that you intend to tinker with reality to suit your purpose – and, perhaps, for the sake of sales. I have to say that, when real people are involved – people to whom, for all I know, you may have a duty to be kind – this strikes me as a very dubious kind of power.'

I'm tempted to say that if he's envious of it in any way he should start work on his own memoirs, but I tell him instead that he should be encouraged by the fact that sales seem to be one of my concerns.

Then, judging that we've been talking about literary strategy for long enough, I ask him whether he'll advance me the £5,000 I need to spring the King of Spain. At first I think he's going to do a Donald Albery on me ('Bad time to borrow . . . rising interest rates . . . negative equity . . . book trade in recession . . . blah blah blah'), but he surprises me by saying that, because of my past record and excellent prospects, he'll be happy to advance me the money I need.

'I'm delighted,' he says, 'that things seem to be going so well for you.'

'Thank you. I think I can honestly say that they've never gone better.'

I return home in a mood of some elation, greatly bucked that this obviously shrewd young man doesn't think I've had it. Equally, I'm resolved not to let him down. I'll not spend a penny of the Listening Bank's money on crack-brained schemes to free the King of Spain. I'll husband it carefully and spend it on my baby.

I interview the Old Etonian writer, Robin Cook, for the *Evening Standard*. It's lunchtime at the Coach And Horses and my assumptions are all comfortably in place, the first one – based on the CV (class traitor, Soho *habitué*, minor criminal) – being that he'll turn up late, if at all.

Not that his participation will be a necessary condition of the interview's success. I've composed it already, have decided to use Cook (and what I assume will be his slogan – that the 'work' must first be 'lived') as a paradigm of the romantic fallacy. And if he does turn up I'll give him a lecture on fiction and the imagination; might even point out that were Jeff Bernard, say, a proper writer (I take him as an example simply because of this unpleasant locale and because Bernard might, all too possibly, be a friend of Cook's I think) he would be able to work in an insurance office and, in the evening, construct his stuff as a work of fiction.

And I look at my watch and decide that I might also give him a burst on the subject of morality and etiquette, point out that the first step is to be polite, which is pretending to be moral. I'll tell him that, never mind broken marriages (five in his case) and unpaid bills, it isn't polite to keep busy people waiting in places like the Coach And Horses – least of all people whose probity has just been guaranteed by Mr Zeberdee of the Midland Bank, Sloane Square, in the sum of £5,000.

So, I'm sitting here cheek by jowl with gymshoed sound technicians and elderly lunchtime playwrights with nicotine-stained hair and a damp patch on their trouser-legs and suddenly Cook is standing at my table – an immensely frail old party in a beret (which in itself is irritating somehow). However, he apologizes most sweetly for keeping me waiting, and we discuss the traffic and the weather, and anyone overhearing us would take us to be two constipated old gents – Nigel Nicolson, say, and his conceited friend the literary hoaxer Humphrey Berkeley – fulfilling a rendezvous at the Garrick Club. For some reason I decide to make this point to Cook.

'We could be mistaken,' I say, 'for Nigel Nicolson and his friend Humphrey Berkeley – the latter, incidentally, being the most unpleasant man I've ever met.'

Cook, who hasn't heard of him, I think, smiles politely and, because I want to set him up as a pub stereotype immediately, I ask him whether this is a place where one might expect to meet interesting people. To my surprise, he says it isn't.

'Ghastly, isn't it?' he says. 'As I say in *The Hidden Files*, even before I get there I can see that hell is going to be a noisy place. Like a pub, it's designed to cover interior silence, whereas happiness reveals silence as the best thing. If you can hear it and bear it.'

I haven't come all this way to hear someone talking about interior silence – still less quoting from his own work – so I draw him back on course by observing, quite sourly, that I would have expected him to be quite at ease in a pub.

'And so I am, old chap,' he says, 'and so I am. I sometimes think that beer, not danger, is the real love of my life.'

That's more like it. Beer and danger – exactly what a sensible man would avoid at any cost. I feel my indigestion coming on, wonder why we couldn't have met somewhere pleasant – the Soda Fountain at Fortnum and Mason, say. When my friend J. P. Donleavy and I feel like holding a writer's workshop we meet in the Soda Fountain at Fortnum and Mason and we have a raspberry milkshake each and a round of watercress sandwiches. We don't need beer and danger to kickstart the imagination.

'But these dreadful people,' I say. 'Do you use them as material?'

Cook seems to be quite shocked by this. 'Certainly not!' he says. 'People should never be used as means. Kant, was it? These are my friends. I enjoy them for themselves.'

Since I myself, and *vis-à-vis* my memoirs, am working in the area of betrayal – or thinking about it, at least – I'm about to ask Cook whether he betrays his friends in *The Hidden Files*. Luckily I realize in time that this would reveal that I haven't read it, so I change the subject.

'Why do you come here, then?'

'To have fun. In the long run, nothing's fun, of course.'

'Nor it is,' I say. 'Nor it is. This will interest you, however. I once fucked Jeff Bernard's second wife – well, more than once, several times, in fact.'

Why did I say that? I'm as surprised as Cook appears to be. I'm bored to tears already, I suppose, and such indiscretions are the conversational equivalent of mooning. I'd rather be vulgar than be bored to tears. It crosses my mind that this is what Pete the Schnoz had warned against. Or is it? And where is my Schnoz in any case? He should have been back from Bangkok days ago. Still, thinking about him now acts as a shot across my bows. I mustn't pursue the matter of Jeff Bernard's second wife. My lips on that subject will be sealed.

'That's right,' I say. 'The first time was at Pratt's Hotel, Bath. As a favour to MGM I put on a play which they intended to film. It was written by two of their best contract writers – Irving Ravetch and Harriet Frank Junior. *Hud*, that was one of theirs. When filmed this play would star Paul Newman and Joanne Woodward, so I cast it with George Baker, Juliet Mills and Jeff Bernard's second wife, Jackie Ellis. And that screwed up MGM's plans, I can tell you.

'Anyway – after the first night in Bath, Sir John Mills and his wife took us out to dinner. Quite a boring evening, as I recall, but after it Jackie Ellis followed me up to my bedroom in Pratt's Hotel. I was quite chuffed at the time, but later I gathered that she made a habit of this sort of thing – a consequence of being married to Jeff Bernard, no doubt.

'By the end of the tour Jackie Ellis and I were resolved to set up house together – an arrangement obliging her to leave her husband and me to leave my wife.

'I can still see my wife crying on the doorstep, and she was holding my boy, Charlie, aged one, and he was crying too, and I moved into the Basil Street Hotel, where they have a Bible by the bedside and where Jackie Ellis was due to join me two days later.

'She never turned up, so I read the Bible for a couple of days and then I went back to my wife. When I next saw Jackie Ellis she told me that we had been ships that pass in the night; further, that she had decided to stay with her drunken husband who had sworn to her that he intended to become a writer. So she was disappointed in that regard, as in many others, too, I wouldn't wonder.

'Be that as it may, I was never able after this to take myself entirely seriously. It's difficult to take yourself very seriously if you've left your wife and one-year-old son crying on the doorstep – thereafter reading the Bible at the Basil Street Hotel while you wait for Jeff Bernard's second wife to join you.'

Cook seems a little mystified by this and, realizing that I have gone on at quite excessive length about myself, I apologize – offering as an excuse the fact that I'm easily bored.

'Are you easily bored?' I ask.

'Oh yes,' he says. 'I've spent much of my adult life studying bores, and I've come to the conclusion that the bore bears a close relationship with the assassin. The bore and the killer are both engaged in the blind pursuit of power. Power is the best shield that the disordered personality can conceive against being revealed as the laughing stock he secretly suspects himself to be. The greatest danger the bore represents is that he makes a bee-line for public life.'

I consider, briefly, the killers I know – Frankie Fraser, the Krays, Jimmy O'Connor, Johnnie Bindon, the Mafia man who, when we were shooting *Root Into Europe*, protected us in Rome – and conclude that I don't agree with the first part of Cook's proposition in the least. Frank's a bit straight, he can be quite disapproving if you don't behave yourself, but he's the least boring person I've ever met. If you want a laugh and a good night out Frank's the man. Jimmy O'Connor can go on a bit, but he isn't exactly boring. The Mafia man in Rome seemed decent enough, and his demands were entirely reasonable – merely that six of his girlfriends appear as extras, albeit in a scene that required no extras. Certainly, he wasn't boring. Bindon was a frightful fucking bore, but I decide that he's the exception to the rule. As for the Krays, we're mere acquaintances (I've only spoken to Reggie briefly on the telephone when he rings Frank from Maidstone, and I can't have met Ron on more than three occasions), but neither has struck me as being boring.

Bad at casting, yes (as bad, almost, as the Head of Light Entertainment at the BBC, who once gave me a beefy lecture on comedy and then, since we were discussing *Root Into Europe*, suggested that Root should be played by Nigel Havers), but boring, no.

I wouldn't, as a rule, front up to Ronnie Kray in the matter of casting, but one evening in 1964 I was obliged to do just that, since I was mounting *Nights at the Comedy* with my Barclaycard, which had fallen temporarily into Mr Kray's possession.

With Mrs Mouse, Birmingham Paul and Birmingham Paul's bodyguard, Winston – a large, scholarly-looking man who spoke in a sinister, asthmatic whisper (the result, I believe, of an old gangland war wound to the windpipe) – I went one evening to Verdi's Grey Topper in Covent Garden, though I can't imagine why. I suppose it was the sort of thing one did with Mrs Mouse. I didn't expect any bother, nor would I have been concerned had bother cropped up. Some months earlier a pop promoter who was about to mount a concert in a famously rough part of Birmingham had asked me to advise him on security. I'd put the matter in the hands of Birmingham Paul, who said he'd give the job to Winston.

'Just Winston?' I'd said.

'Winston,' Birmingham Paul had said, 'is more than a match for a few hundred Birmingham herberts.'

I was sitting contentedly at Verdi's Grey Topper, then, when a fight broke out on the dance floor. It seemed to be in slow motion, as in a comic western. Large men in Cecil Gee suits a size too small fisted pillars and sailed headfirst into pyramids of bottles. A very small waiter was hit on the nose, spun through 360 degrees and hit on the nose again. Mr Verdi appealed for order and had his hat knocked off. The band played on.

I was enjoying myself, didn't for some time realize that the fight was real. Then Winston tipped us off.

'It's the twins,' he croaked. 'We'd better get out.' He had more respect for Ronnie and Reggie, clearly, than for a few hundred Birmingham hooligans in a rented disco.

I called for the bill, paid with my Barclaycard, made for the exit. Then I realized that I'd left my Barclaycard behind. I had plans to mount a musical with my Barclaycard – *Nights at the Comedy*, starring Nicol Williamson, Ida Barr and Mrs Shufflewick – so there was nothing for it but to return to our table, where Ronnie Kray was now sitting, holding my Barclaycard.

'That's mine,' I said – an odd thing to do, but such was the urgency in those days for credit lines when mounting musicals. 'I'm in show business, you understand. *Nights at the Comedy*, starring Nicol Williamson.'

'A difficult artiste, from all I hear,' said Mr Kray. 'Lose him and get the new boy, Tarbuck, that's my advice.'

Bad at casting, yes, but not obviously boring. And the odd thing is that, years later, when filming *Root Into Europe* in Rome, I happened to ask the Mafia man who was protecting us what he thought of the show so far.

'*Ha considerato Nigel Havers per il ruolo di Rooto?*' he asked.

I didn't feel inclined to listen, having learnt my lesson about taking casting advice from killers. *Nights at the Comedy* had opened in 1964 with Jimmy Tarbuck in place of Nicol Williamson and had flopped nastily a few weeks later.

So, sitting in the Coach And Horses with Robin Cook, the Old Etonian writer, I don't agree with him that the bore bears a close relationship with the assassin. I do agree with him, however, that power is the best shield that the disordered personality can conceive against being revealed as the laughing stock he secretly suspects himself to be; further, that the greatest danger the bore represents is that he makes a bee-line for public life.

On the other hand, and judging it important that I come across in the interview as cleverer than Cook, I see an opportunity here not only to turn Cook's conclusion on its head (by pointing out that it's equally a symptom of the disordered personality, and a shield against feelings of insignificance, determinedly to *present* yourself as a laughing stock) but also, in due course, to introduce an illustrative anecdote useful for my memoirs when I come to write them.

Accordingly I ask Cook whether he's temperamentally opposed to all forms of authority.

'Oh yes,' he says.

'It's your view that we should rock the boat whenever possible?'

'Absolutely.'

He's walked into my trap. With the help of an anecdote involving Professor Anthony Storr – to be trotted out again at the appropriate moment in my memoirs – I'll show Cook that rebels like him are simply pests.

'That's what I used to think,' I say. 'Once, at Winchester, the school corps was being inspected by a desert general – the Auk at a guess. It would be amusing, I thought, to turn left every time our platoon commander, my friend Grafftey-Smith, gave the order to turn right. I made a nonsense of the whole thing, do you see? My housemaster Mr Emmett later carpeted me in his study. He was squinting with rage. He feared for my future, he said, and meanwhile I would have to be thrashed by the head boy – a threat I didn't take particularly seriously since I was the head boy.'

'You were the head boy?'

'In fact, I wasn't. But here's the point: some years later, when I was writing an article about the authoritan personality, I went to see Anthony Storr in Oxford. I told him how, at Winchester, I'd turned left instead of right in front of the Auk, whereupon he said that the instinctive rebel was as unbalanced in his way as the instinctive authoritarian. There are many situations, said Storr, in which rocking the boat would simply be irrational – after a shipwreck in a rough sea, for instance.

'That had never occurred to me. It was the best advice I'd ever received, and since then I have always lived my life in accordance with Storr's principle: if in doubt, play it by the rules. A little boring, perhaps, a little straight up and down, a little humdrum, but I make no apology for that.'

In fact, I'm quite surprised by this small speech. Being taken seriously by Mr Zeberdee of the Midland Bank, Sloane Square, rather than anything said by Professor Storr, seems to have radically altered the way I see things. Cook, and people like him, would never get an unsecured facility from Mr Zeberdee. I now look at him sternly and ask him whether this attitude of his hasn't damaged a lot of people – friends, wives, tradesmen.

'I suppose it must have done,' he says.

'You're utterly feckless, then? I imagine you've left behind a trail of disappointed people. The Inland Revenue? The VAT man, perhaps? Have you paid the VAT man?'

'I'm never in one place long enough for him to catch up with me.'

They'll catch him soon enough, they always do. I don't bother to point this out. I register my disapproval by raising an eyebrow slightly. I'm the representative here of officialdom, of brown envelopes, of the uncelebrated virtues of suburbia, of small shop-keepers who have paid their bills and upon whom people like Cook are, in the long run, parasitical.

'The fact is,' he continues, 'I try to reduce life to its essentials.'

'And they're not essential? Wives? Friends?'

'I suppose not.'

'That sounds very cold. Are you cold?'

'Not cold, I think. Absent, rather.'

He gives the impression that he knows what he means by this – something to do, I think, with this dispiriting canard: that the writer has better things to do than become engaged by the daily business of domestic maintenance.

And now, satisfied with a job well done, I leave him – calling in on the way home at the Midland Bank, Sloane Square, to dip into my new facility. I'm quite tempted to withdraw £5,000 now – spending the lot on a treat for me and my baby which will have us reaching for our brains – but I spot Mr Zeberdee loitering behind the tellers, so I cash a cheque for just £200. I don't want Mr Zeberdee to think that I'm bad at money management. I greet him cheerily and inform him that I've just been on an assignment for the *Evening Standard*.

'Things are going better and better,' he says.

'Indeed they are,' I reply.

Later, at home, I glance through *The Hidden Files* and notice that Cook, with apparent approval, quotes Cyril Connolly as saying that if a man wrote honestly about himself he'd produce a masterpiece – a characteristically metropolitan, and empty, contribution to literary journalism and a question-begging one at that, since it assumes that we know the truth about ourselves.

I discover, too, that the title of the book refers to a computer's array of hidden files – files which hold the functions that make it the subtle machine it is: memory, comparison, exchange, replace, obliterate, restore, etc. Cook points out that these files, which are written in symbolic language, are never shown to the viewer, who, in any case, wouldn't understand them even if they were. The machine knows that it is not necessary to show them, except to an expert, who has access to the hidden files should the machine break down.

Cook is claiming, I suppose, that a writer is, uniquely, both a computer and a computer expert, with access, unlike the ordinary person, to the infinite complexity of his hidden files; further, and less controversially – indeed the insight is obvious to say the least – that a writer's performance is judged on the final visible quality of the output rather than on the obscure cryptic processes that contributed to it. While I'd dispute the suggestion that a writer has an expert's access to his own hidden files, I might look at the whole question in my memoirs.

★

I wake up feeling strangely calm. As a rule, I find it best to confront the fact of consciousness speedily and at an angle, to get quickly out of bed and thereafter move faster than myself – faster at least than I can think. I spin in small circles, trying to move faster than the facts, and then I make myself a cup of coffee. By the time I've drunk this the facts are manageable, more or less.

This morning, however, I lie quietly in bed, feeling quite peaceful; it's a feeling of relief, really, almost of euphoria, though I can't at first identify its cause. Then, suddenly, it all comes back to me – and the reason, too, for this unaccustomed sense of ease. I have had a strange, almost endlessly extended dream – more a nightmare, really – and my relief is a function of this discovery: that a dream is all it was.

I have dreamt that Mrs Lamb of the Inland Revenue has made me bankrupt. I realize, in my dream, that from the daily nausea of brown envelopes I must have opened one too few; that I have refused later to open the door once too often to a burly man in a pork-pie hat, armed with a Statutory Demand. This morning, in my dream, I received a letter from something called the Insolvency Service informing me that I was bankrupted a week ago in the High Court on the application of Mrs Lamb.

Floating luxuriously in this warm sea of relief – that it was just a dream – I go over the curiously extended details in my mind. My first thought, in my dream – experienced sickeningly as if from a sudden physical assault – was that this was the end of the road for me and Penny, my beloved, an end to gorgeous nights of chaos and sensation. My beloved isn't particularly acquisitive – indeed, she has rather a relaxed attitude to money – but unless I could look after her what on earth would be the point of me?

My second and almost as alarming thought concerned my new friend and mentor Mr Zeberdee of the Midland Bank, Sloane Square. Convinced, only a few days ago, of my financial probity and promise, he advanced me £5,000, only to discover this morning that I'm bankrupt.

Then, in my dream, I suddenly grew cunning. *Would* he have discovered it yet? I could feel my lips curling ravenously like an urban fox with the scent of a fat farmyard pullet in its nostrils. I calculate, in my dream, that my assets might not have been frozen yet. I might have time to slink along to Sloane Square and inflict terrible damage on the Midland Bank plc. I'd be in and out like a fox in a hen-coop. I'd leave my friend Mr Zeberdee featherless and bleeding.

I dressed appropriately for the matter in hand – in my dream I even wore a fox's head, acquired, I imagine, from a theatrical costumier – switched on the answering-machine and prepared to lope along to Sloane Square dressed as a fox, when I was stopped by the telephone ringing. It was a Mr Letts of the *Daily Telegraph* who wanted me to call him back. I'd never heard of a Mr Letts, so I rang him back, wearing my fox's head, and he said how sorry he was to read in the *London Gazette* that I'd been bankrupted by Mrs Lamb of the Inland Revenue.

That knocked the stuffing out of me. My disgrace would now be advertised all over the *Daily Telegraph*. Worse, it was too late, obviously, to gain a pecuniary advantage over the Midland Bank plc. They too would have read the *London Gazette* by now. If, dressed as a fox, I tried to finesse the Midland Bank plc out of £5,000 I'd be collared in the foyer.

In my dream this realization knocked me for the moment off my feet. In my dream I went back to bed – where I dozed fitfully, cruelly held just this side of unconsciousness by the hideous scenario ahead. I'd have no money at all. Mrs Lamb would take the lot. How would I survive? Nothing in my background had prepared me for this. At Winchester there'd been nothing about this in 'Budge' Firth's sermon to the leavers. I wasn't in the least an urban fox bred for survival in a concrete jungle. According to 'Budge' Firth, I was a finely tuned Rolls-Royce; a Rolls-Royce, in this case, that urgently needed a push start from a humble Morris Minor.

I'd have to pass the hat around among Morris Minors of my acquaintance, put the bite on streetwise chaps who (perhaps because they hadn't been to Winchester) always have a bankroll up their sleeves. That would be OK; I'd levy a sudden and retrospective surcharge on my friendship down the years; oblige them to recompense me for listening politely to their uneducated views. Nor would they mind at all, I think. As humble Morris Minors they'd be spitefully grateful for this unexpected chance to feel superior. Accordingly, and in my dream, I drew up a list of streetwise people – Honest John, Black Simone, Fat Pat, Jillypoo, Steve the Stud and June Upstairs – whose privilege it would be to help me out.

There was worse to come, however, as I now realized in my dream. There'd be a series of humiliating meetings at the offices of the Insolvency Service. I'd be quizzed impertinently by a Mr Chillery, a malevolent little fuck in an outlandish suit and wearing a ring on the wrong finger. Mr Chillery wouldn't understand my lifestyle in the least.

'Perhaps you'd like to tell me how this state of affairs occurred?' he'd say.

'And perhaps you'd like a smack in the face, you common little twerp,' I'd say.

Or would I adopt a submissive posture, admit that this pretty pass was a consequence of my addiction? No – I could never do that, I think. I could never offer that fraudulent defence – least of all to a petty investigator who wore a ring on the wrong finger.

Counsellors called Liz in seaside clinics like to say that addiction's a disease. Those of us fortunate enough to have been raised in Sunningdale know better. Addiction, we know – least of all addiction to silent performing women – is never a disease. It's a choice, or a refusal; a refusal to help yourself. You know you're in trouble, but there's no alternative – no alternative at least that might make you occasionally happy. So, in Sunningdale, if you were on the ropes you boxed on. You squared the shoulders and walked the high street with your toes turned out. You didn't go into therapy, hold hands in a group and put your faith in Him up there. You cracked on. Nor will anything have changed. Search Sunningdale today from end to end and you'll not find anyone in bits, I'll wager, holding hands in a group or putting their faith in Him up there.

Still less do you go into therapy if, like me, you've been to Winchester; if, like me, you've been addressed on the subject of attitude – in War Cloisters and on a misty November afternoon – by a desert general, sometimes the Auk, sometimes Wavell.

At Winchester there was a custom called a Bross Blow. If your attitude was wrong, you could, by medieval statute, be punched in the stomach by a senior from a measured distance. A senior, judging that your attitude was wrong, could punch you senseless. My housemaster, Mr Emmett, was obliged, when entering hall for evening prayers, to pick his way carefully over the bodies of little boys laid low by Bross Blows.

In a nutshell, you don't, if you were born in Sunningdale, later, and at an impressionable age, being addressed on attitude by a desert general and punched thereafter in the stomach, claim that addiction's a disease and book yourself into a seaside clinic – as no doubt I'd shortly be explaining to Mr Chillery in the offices of the Insolvency Service.

Then, in my dream, I slept for a while but was woken suddenly by a ring at the doorbell. It was dark outside. I must have slept all day. I answered the door – something I'd only have done in a dream – and there was a courier with a bottle of champagne from Mr Letts of the *Daily Telegraph*. Even in dreams, it seems, people of good background know how to be kind when it matters.

'Thank you,' I said in my dream.

'You're wearing a fox's head,' said the courier.

'I'm well aware of that,' I said.

And then, in my dream, I noticed that there were five messages on my answering machine, so I played them back and discovered that they were all from Penny, my beloved. And although I'd been dreading this moment I realized that I'd have to let her in on the terrible news eventually, so I rang her back.

'God, I was so *worried*,' she said in my dream. 'I thought something dreadful had happened.'

'It has.'

'Christ, what?'

'I'm bankrupt.'

In my dream Penny was silent for what seemed an eternity. I thought she'd hung up in disgust, had decided to be done with me immediately. Then she let out a great gasp of relief.

'*Never* do that again!' she said. 'God – I thought you were going to tell me something awful.'

'It is awful,' I said.

'Why? It's only money. I've got money. Do you need money? I know – I've got the answer! My Barclays Connect card! You can have it! You'll be able to take out £250 a day! That will solve the problem. I'll bring it over now. I'll be there in half an hour.'

At which point I must have woken up, since I can remember nothing more. So I lie in bed, turning over the details of this peculiar dream in my mind and wondering whether, in reality, Penny would have come up trumps as she had in my dream. And, deciding that she wouldn't, I regret for the first time that it had been merely a dream, that I've been cheated of discovering that my baby is, after all, an angel.

And then I notice that it's light outside and that there is the noise of cars and people in the street, so I look at my watch and discover, to my astonishment, that it's 4 p.m. I've slept through a whole day – may even have missed a day – which is quite unlike me.

I stumble out of bed, sway slightly – and this is unusual, too; I don't in the morning sway as a rule – and go to the kitchen, where I make myself a cup of coffee.

And then I move into the living-room with my cup of coffee and

I put it down on the table next to an empty bottle of champagne, which has a note on it identifying it as a gift from the *Daily Telegraph*. And next to it is a champagne-stained letter from a Mr Chillery of the Insolvency Service informing me that I've been bankrupted by Mrs Lamb of the Inland Revenue and asking me to keep an appointment with him at 2 p.m. in three weeks' time. And next to this is Penny's Connect card with a scribbled message, saying: 'Here's your card! Don't you dare lose it! Sleep well – see you tomorrow.'

And this is very frightening. I sit down, lean back, close my eyes and breathe deeply. All the events of my dream have really happened, but try, as I do now, to focus them more clearly they still have only the shape and substance of a dream. Nor do I have any recollection – dream-like or otherwise – of Penny coming over. The last thing I remember, but as a dream, is talking to her on the telephone.

I might at this point have lost my reason had not the explanation suddenly come to me – not as a memory but as a logical deduction. I must, on receipt of the letter from Mr Chillery, have gone into shock; I must have taken a handful of Rohypnols and retired to bed, experiencing subsequent events (some of them, at least) as if in a dream, and, in this respect, doing better than Pete the Schnoz, who, after two Rohypnols, has no memory at all.

Since the worst part of this catastrophe – telling Penny – seems to have been successfully, indeed advantageously, negotiated, I summon up the courage to ring her now – to ask her, somewhat apprehensively, what happened last night after she came over.

And she's her usual happy, bubbly self, and she tells me it was quite hilarious, that we drank the champagne from Mr Letts of the *Telegraph* and that I then took a handful of Rohypnols – thereafter reeling around like a safari park rhino shot with a Valium dart. She managed to steer me towards the bedroom, she said, after which she left – leaving her Connect card on the coffee-table.

Thinking that bankruptcy is a small price to pay for the discovery that my baby is, after all, an angel, and because I still feel a little groggy, I return to bed.

I have always supposed that a writer can never experience his own stuff as others do – any more than we can experience ourselves as objects. A writer can't surprise himself, admiringly catch his own attention and think to himself: My word! I didn't know that. He can attempt to criticize his stuff, of course, stand back and try to judge its impact – but the reader's experience can never be his.

Well, it can if he doses himself with enough Rohypnol an hour or two before retiring for the night. I'm quite surprised this morning to find in my writer's notebook a long, almost illegible message to myself which I have no recollection of having written. Only by checking the Rohypnol bottle (three more are missing) can I be sure that I must have scribbled it last night before I went to bed.

NB MEMOIRS [it says]. Refer to Helmut Newton story. Eighteen-year-old Berlin banker's daughter grossly naked under fur coat in opulent tea-room of grand hotel. Quote Sartre. Slime and nausea. The contingency of existence entails its obscenity. Our being derives from our experience of others as *subjects*. The other gazes at me and in virtue of her gaze I find myself a person. I acquire a Nature. That nature I cannot disown. Hence Sartre's point about sado-masochism. The master–slave relationship. An attempt to experience the subjectivity of the beloved. Is that it? Look it up. (Easier: check Scruton on Sartre. Do tomorrow.)

Refer to Annie Ross on way to airport. She tells me that the sixties won't start until 1967. She says that Jacqui the Dancer won't be a suitable person to do the sixties with. 'She's not flaky enough,' she says. 'Dancers have got their heads screwed on. You'll need a

Mrs Mouse.' Until Mrs Mouse, nothing but guilt and nausea. But Mrs Mouse was a civilian really. She wanted a nice dressing-table and to give dinner-parties featuring *coq au vin* more than she wanted to be fucked on the wrong side of a two-way mirror by pop musicians at one of Janie Jones's parties. In this respect she let me down.

And so it was a sequence of civilians. Jacqui the Dancer and the Polaroids. How unlike her! A *soloiste* with the Royal Ballet grossly naked amid the ordinary furnishings of a daytime service flat. How embarrassing! How inappropriate! Pauline Boty and Sonya Dean – their mirrored voluptuousness snapped and walleted by me. Sarah finds the Polaroids. Her uncomprehending fury: 'I'd have done that if you'd asked me to.' Sobbing under the bedclothes. She didn't understand. I *loved* her. (Ironic. Don't, in memoirs, mention Mr Emmett, Pode or Winchester again. The reader will have got the point by now.) And Carly Simon? Stretched out and naked at the Basil Street Hotel, where they place a Bible by the bedside. The pouting centrefold's reference to Hefner. How unbecoming! How out of character! She was a serious person – real and richly gifted.

And so it was Mrs Mouse, *then* Melanie and an end at last to nausea and guilt. Then Penny. (And Michelle? Don't know yet.) Mention the fact that I was interviewed by a quack in a seaside clinic. The quack says: 'I can cure Melanie, but I can't cure you.' Silly cunt. where will that go? And somewhere I must include a snatch of cautionary talk with Penny. Me: 'Why don't we risk it? See if we can?' Penny: 'We will. Next time. Next time we'll be good. We'll go out to dinner. We'll have Chinese and talk. *Really* talk. Like we used to. I miss our talks. Can I have another? A really big one? Then I'll be good.' Penny will have to get away. I wonder if she knows this?

I can't make head nor tail of this, and this is frustrating since I feel it's significant in some way, that I may – to borrow an analogy due to the thriller writer Robin Cook – have been given a Rohypnol-induced glimpse of my hidden files.

Be that as it may, I now make myself a cup of coffee and reread my recently discovered hidden files – if that is what they are – calmly from the top. Helmut Newton? I admire him greatly, of course, but I know nothing about an eighteen-year-old banker's daughter naked in the tea-room of an opulent hotel. I move hastily past Sartre and Scruton, since I'm in no condition to puzzle their stuff out, and have arrived at the reference to Jacqui the Dancer when the telephone rings. It's my best friend, Little Jo.

'Are you all right?' she says.

'I think so. Why?'

'You sounded drunk last night.'

'*Me? Drunk?* When?'

'When you telephoned me.'

'I *telephoned* you? Are you sure?'

'Absolutely certain. It was quite late. You woke me up. You were going on and on about Helmut Newton and an eighteen-year-old banker's daughter in the tea-room of a grand hotel. And she didn't have a stitch on! Imagine! I mean! You wanted me to come over wearing nothing but high heels and a fur coat. Do you want to hear more?'

I feel sick. Little Jo is a judge's daughter, she's Deputy Editor of *Tatler*, she attends receptions with a matching boy from Hambro's and sometimes, on Friday, she rings me up and asks whether by any chance I'll be in London over the weekend, for all the world as if I might be off to Gloucestershire. For these reasons I hold to the belief that while Little Jo has a good opinion of me I'm not entirely done for. And now, it seems, I have told her that I would like to see her stark naked except for high heels and her reading glasses.

'You were very insistent about the reading glasses,' she says.

I apologize as best I can, and Little Jo seems to have taken this depressing incident in her stride; indeed, she seems to regard it as comic as much as anything, and she suggests that we have lunch in ten days' time. So that's all right.

But then this thought occurs: on Rohypnol, clearly, one is as much at the mercy of one's dark unconscious as a hypnotized stooge from the audience ridiculed on stage by a cabaret artiste. I'm fortunate, perhaps, that I didn't discover something worse about myself: that I wanted, say, to run around quacking like a duck. At least my request to Little Jo was in character, if dismally unbecoming.

The first thing, obviously, is to flush the Rohypnol down the lavatory, but while I'm searching for them another thought occurs: without them I may never crack the meaning of my recently dis covered hidden files, which continue to seem significant. Having first disconnected the telephone as a precaution against further obscene calls to virtuous girls whose fathers work in chambers, might it not be sensible to take Rohypnol again tonight, thereafter, and in the morning, inspecting my writer's notebook to discover whether my hidden files have been added to – or, better still, interpreted?

It's a risk worth taking, I think, in the interests of self-discovery. It might even solve the technical problem of embarrassment. On Rohypnol I seem uninhibited enough to confront the secrets in my hidden files, to betray people who were close to me and dwell gaudily on private inclinations.

Pratley telephones to confirm our rendezvous on Friday.

'What rendezvous?' I say.

'Don't tell me you've forgotten. You and your baby are bringing Saffy the Page Three Scorcher down to the Rat And Carrot in Battersea. You confirmed it on Monday.'

This is frightening. I've no recollection of this at all. And I thought today was Monday.

'What day is it today?'

'Wednesday,' says Pratley.

Wednesday? I've lost two days somewhere. I've been on the Rohypnol again without realizing it – not that you can be on it *and* realize it, I suppose, this being the point of them. Monday must have been the night I telephoned Little Jo and said I'd like to see her in nothing but high heels and her reading glasses. Presumably, I also confirmed the rendezvous with Saffy and Pratley. That's two more nights of mad telephone calls I don't remember making and messages to myself in my writer's notebook. I manage to maintain a breezy front for Pratley.

'Of course, of course,' I say. 'See you on Friday. What time did we say?'

'Nine o'clock,' he replies.

Then, and with some anxiety, I ring up Penny, my beloved – fearful that, because of the Rohypnol, I may have forgotten to mention the rendezvous to her. She, as usual, is positive and bubbly, and she quickly reassures me. She's a radiator, my baby; she makes everyone feel better always.

'I can hardly wait!' she says. 'I'm really looking forward to it!'

We have a few laughs at Pratley's expense, about his uninteresting, married man's serial randiness – and then Penny, becoming suddenly solemn, admits that there's something she's been keeping from me. Her fat man from Cornwall wants to take her to Mauritius for two weeks on Saturday – the day after our night out with Pratley and Saffy the Page Three Scorcher.

'Do you mind?' she says.

This is tricky. Her contempt for her fat man is such that I don't mind in the least, but I have to pretend to mind a bit. In fact, I'd prefer it, in a sickening sort of way, if she was going away with someone she liked – with Tracey, her beloved, say. That, while horrifying, would be quite exciting.

And while I'm thinking this, something quite eerie happens. My brain does a kind of loop and I lose my grip on the present. The sensation is stranger than mere *déjà vu*; I'm in an alternative reality; I'm

161

in Sarah's house in Hasker Street and she's standing at the foot of the bed, head bowed in sweet remorse and saying, a trifle too theatrically, 'I'm guilty.'

And this is a sudden glimpse into my hidden files, I think, and then Sarah's vanished and I'm back in the present and Penny's speaking.

'Hey! Are you still there? Are you listening?'

'Sorry. What?'

'I said, do you mind?'

'Mind what?'

'Golly! If I go to Mauritius with my fat man?'

I wish I did. I'd like to feel that lovely stab of jealousy, the sharpest thrill of all. But this isn't possible with Penny's fat man. If I mention him, she pulls a face – refuses to say more than that she has to feign sleep in the morning and when out of doors walk ten yards behind him in the street in case people mistake them for a couple. I should be offended by his fat and financed early-morning fumblings, but I'm not. *My* Penny isn't present. The fat man's on his own, though he doesn't know it.

'Of course I mind,' I say.

'I won't go, then.'

This is a step in our witty ritual. She knows that I can't stop her going – or, rather, that I could stop her but that neither of us would care to test the consequence of this. I'd not want that responsibility, and she'd not want to give it to me.

'I do need the money,' she says.

And now I feel guilty. If I were better organized she wouldn't have to do these things. She wouldn't have to fly around the world with a fat man who has a camcorder and an agenda and a guide to sites of historical interest. Nor would she have to feign sleep in the morning to evade his hotel suite fumblings. If I were better organized I'd steal money from my wife and put it secretly into Penny's account – an account, which, happily, will be topped up shortly by her fat man for services rendered in Mauritius and one to which, thanks to her Connect card, I now have access. I realize suddenly that I have access to the fat man's money! This makes me feel a little better.

And now we play another of our amusing games. Whenever Penny goes away, and in order to feel closer to her, I always switch my watch to whatever time zone she happens to be in – a habit which started after I had a religious experience in 1988. That summer, in Ibiza, we took some ecstasy together and, while I felt fine – ecstatic, in fact – Penny got the horrors.

She lay on the bed and for the next five hours I sat on the bed and gazed down at her with feelings of such love and admiration that I decided soon enough that no materialistic interpretation of the world could account for them.

Suddenly Dummett's argument for God seemed as irrefutable as it is elegant. We know there is value, Dummett argues (we *know* that torturing people is wrong as certainly as we know that this is a chair and that a table), but value, unlike tables and chairs, isn't part of the world. So someone must have put it there, and this could only be a Supreme Being. Equally, and as I gazed down with adoration at my baby, I understood that my feelings for her couldn't be part of the world. Only a belief in a transcendent being could account for them.

All nonsense, of course (a first-year student could drive a coach and horses through Professor Dummett's argument), but the next day, when Penny flew to Florida on business, I, in my new, albeit ecstasy-induced, religious frame of mind, was certain of one thing only: that while she was away there must be perfect synchronicity in how we experienced the world.

I couldn't endure the thought that I might be awake while she was sleeping or, worse – since I wouldn't be able to watch over her from a distance – vice versa. For the next two weeks I went on to Florida time – and this, to someone as habitually punctual as myself, was a great inconvenience, since it entailed my being eight hours late at every rendezvous. It's all right if she flies on business in an easterly direction, since this causes me to be even earlier for a date than usual, but if she flies west it plays havoc with my schedule.

'Where's Mauritius?' I ask. 'Not in the Caribbean, I hope.'

'It's off Africa, I think.'

'Thank God for that. I'll be ahead in my arrangements when I go on to Mauritius time.'

'Don't go on it yet!' she says. 'You'd look silly turning up five hours early for our date with Saffy!'

And after we've hung up I search around for my writer's notebook, fearful of what, as a consequence of my lost nights on Rohypnol, I may find added to my hidden files. The almost illegible message to myself is shorter this time but just as baffling.

'NB MEMOIRS,' it says. Then there's some quite vulgar stuff about women as objects ('Passive. Compliant. Harnessed and pouched by Anne Summers in the Charing Cross Road,' it says – whatever that may mean), and there's this bald question: 'Who's belittled? Subject or object? See Sartre. Same situation surely as the banker's eighteen-year-old daughter in the Helmut Newton story?'

The Helmut Newton story again, and its connection with anything else as obscure as ever. Then, underlined – so I must think it has some peculiar significance – this: '*Yet for every man who wants to treat women as objects theirs* [sic] *a woman who wants to be one. Hence Saffy on the game.*'

This is followed by some stuff which – happily, perhaps – is illegible, and then, to my surprise, I come to this: 'VERY NB MEMOIRS. In telephone conversation with Penny about her trip to Mauritius with her fat man, introduce deft time-loop idea (cracking up?). Insert sudden image (flashback?) of Sarah admitting guilty liaison with a Frenchman. Emphasize accompanying excitement rather than rage. First experience of jealousy as sharpest of all pleasures. Refer at this point to hidden files.'

This isn't very helpful. I've got self-reference here, ever a source of confusion and antinomies. I hope my hidden files aren't about to play games with me. I don't want to wake up after a night on Rohypnol to find this statement in my hidden files: 'Nothing in my hidden files is true.'

To decipher this, I must keep my head. So – what have I got? I start at the top, move hastily past the crude stuff about compliant women pouched in Soho, briefly consider the Helmut Newton story – which still yields nothing – and pause at the sudden suggestion that Saffy is thinking of going on the game.

This is news to me. I know nothing about any plans Saffy may have in this direction. Some years ago, and awash with indignant, undirected lust, I did telephone her just in case. She was writing her memoirs for the *News of the World*, she said, and she read me an extract involving another Page Three Scorcher. I said something distasteful, to be regretted, and she laughed, not unkindly, I remember. 'You're obviously in a bad way,' she said. 'You'd better meet Melanie.' She sounded like a doctor filling a prescription. She introduced us, but I do not believe she has ever thought of going on the game herself.

So – what else do I have in my hidden files? At the end, there is this odd instruction to myself to conjure up an image of Sarah while talking to Penny on the telephone. And did I? It seems as if the conversation with Penny happened hours ago, but I try to remember how it went.

There was something about her going to Mauritius with her fat man. She asked me if I minded, and I thought: I only wish I did. That at least would be exciting.

And suddenly I've cracked it! Not all of it – I'm still in the dark about Helmut Newton and the banker's daughter, about Saffy being on the game and about the other stuff as well – but all at once I understand what the reference to Sarah means.

And very artful it is – or will be if I include it in my memoirs. In 1965, when Sarah was filming *Those Magnificent Men in Their Flying*

Machines, I got it into my head that she was having an affair – or wanted to have an affair – with an imported Frenchman. One evening she asked me if I'd mind very much if she had dinner with him. 'Don't worry,' she said. 'I'll come straight home afterwards. I'll be back by eleven thirty at the latest.'

It was the longest night of my life. At twelve thirty I went to bed and tossed and turned with my insides in a knot of pain, and there was no pleasure in it in the least. And, at three thirty Sarah, looking as pretty as a picture, as demure as a daisy in a little dress by De Lyss, was suddenly standing at the foot of the bed, head bowed in sweet remorse and saying, rather too theatrically, 'I'm guilty.'

And instantly, to my embarrassment, I wanted her more than I ever had before. I didn't touch her, though. Sarah wasn't a silent performing woman to be held in disgrace, to be stripped to her high heels only and taken angrily against a wall. She was the woman I loved and lived with, with whom I watched television in bed and with whom I walked in Kensington Gardens on summer afternoons.

I still keep a photograph of her taken in the park on a summer afternoon. She must have been just twenty-one and she's wearing a pretty white bikini and she's holding a stick to be retrieved by Addo Reed, her Pyrenean mountain dog.

'This is one of those days,' she said.

'What days?' I said.

'A day one will look back on and think: I was happy that day.'

Thirty years later, it seems odd – sad even – that shortly we were to live our entire lives quite separately, and yet we'd had a day like that. I suppose there must be millions of people who have shared a day like that and are now, for no particular reason perhaps, living their lives quite separately.

In any case I didn't yet know about the gorgeous pain of infidelity, about nursery games and clever punishments. So, on the night of her guilt, I turned away from her and, in all likelihood, thought about tall silent women pacing a stage with nothing on.

This flashback to Sarah during my conversation with Penny – this embarrassing reminder of how ignorant I was until I met Melanie – is quite adroit, I think, and I'll include it in my memoirs.

Abusing the Rohypnol has had another unexpected consequence. It has caused me not to register four vital phone calls, in the customary sequence of six, from Pete the Schnoz – the upshot being that he and I have, at one sitting, done £500 worth of crack bought and put aside for me and my baby.

So here's another lesson learnt in a long life and one to be passed on to young Lovering, or whoever, in my memoirs. Don't put the seals on first and, more importantly, it's usually a mistake to buy your stuff more than a minute ahead of when you plan to use it. Since you'll do it all at once – not least if Pete the Schnoz happens to be in the same country when you score – you'll have finished it, so to speak, before you start.

I now make this mistake, while waiting for the Publisher to return to our table. With tomorrow's rendezvous in mind – and because it will be the last time I see my baby for two whole almost unendurable weeks – I ring around to make sure that the lines of delivery are clear, only to be told that there's an unaccustomed shortage. Jillypoo can't help, nor can Ralph, nor can Andy From The Sixties. I could drop in at Happy's crack-house, but after two close shaves there in the past few weeks I have rather lost my nerve. Andy From The Sixties suggests that I try his fiancée Michelle, but this is silly since she doesn't yet exist. (More accurately, perhaps, she does exist but I haven't met her yet.)

Then I realize that this is a technical difficulty, merely; that, by this point in my memoirs, I may have met her; that she may be about to inherit the inverted commas and the little Katharine Hamnett skirt. It might be clever – and, more importantly, it would solve my current problem – were I to introduce her now. I decide, therefore, to score from her – if only for artistic reasons.

In many respects Michelle is – or will be when I meet her – the paradigmatic other woman: mad milky little legs, tumbling hair, a vicious pout – but she may turn out to be a little too streetwise for me. For one thing there are bullet-holes in the passenger seat of the get-away car, and for another she is sometimes, when doing business, hung upside down by the heels from a high-rise block in Brixton. That doesn't happen in my part of the world. Nothing, in my part of the world, hangs upside down over a balcony but a potted plant grown by the staircase queer. There is, too, the matter of her common-law husband Tommy Roche having been shot in a lay-by in the course of a cocaine dispute.

Nor is that the worst of it. Being streetwise, if Michelle's the model, means that you have an extended family in west London, all of whom are as mad as you are and have a yard, sometimes with cars on it, sometimes not. In spite of this, you seldom have anywhere to live, the car's broken down and you've just been disconnected from the national grid. You drop in on your friends at 5 a.m., having got the worst of a punch-up in Coldharbour Lane. Michelle often drops in at 5 a.m. (or will drop in by the time she makes an appearance in my memoirs) and asks me for her petrol money.

'What petrol money?' I say.

'My petrol money for coming here.'

'But I didn't ask you to come here.'

'So what?' she says. 'I'm here, aren't I?'

Plus, if you ask her for something, no matter what, she always says she's got it. I wouldn't do that. If I was asked for something and I didn't have it, I'd say so – but I'm not streetwise.

'Are you carrying?' I say to Michelle on her mobile phone, which is in the name of her best friend Fat Denise, who, being even more streetwise than Michelle, is, without knowing it, paying for this facility.

'Yes,' she says.

'Where are you now?'

'On the M4,' she says, 'just coming up to Shepherd's Bush round-about.'

Michelle, like other streetwise people, is always on the M4 and approaching Shepherd's Bush roundabout. If a bomb went off at Shepherd's Bush roundabout the drug problem would be solved immediately. Natty men in canary-yellow Rasta hats would be talking to each other on their mobile phones while hanging upside down from trees.

'When can you get here?' I say.

'In twenty minutes,' she replies.

Michelle has never crossed the road in twenty minutes, but I fall for it every time. Two hours later I ring again.

'Where are you now?' I ask.

'In Earls Court,' she says. 'Just around the corner from you.'

If she isn't on the M4 Michelle is always in Earls Court, which isn't in any case just around the corner or anywhere near it. In spite of this, and when she at last turns up – running the last ten yards (tumbling hair, mad milky little legs everywhere at once) – I'm usually glad to see her, or will be glad by the time I start my memoirs. I do ask her, though, why she's always late.

She looks at me impatiently and says: 'Things happen, don't they?'

'Is that part of being streetwise?'

'Of course.'

'Where's the stuff, then?'

'I haven't got it,' she says. 'I told you – things happen. Can I have my petrol money?'

Very endearing, and, notwithstanding the fact that I don't want any confusions of this sort before tomorrow night, I decide for artistic reasons to buy from her on this occasion. Nor, amazingly, does she let me down. She turns up with the stuff more or less on time, but without her legs – a consequence, I think, of an arrangement to meet Andy From The Sixties later. Andy From The Sixties, who is strenuously respectable, prefers her not to show her stocking-tops in public.

'Sorry, I'm not wearing my legs,' she says.

'That's all right. I haven't met you yet.'

'Right.'

'I might, however, need you as an ending.'

'What sodding ending?'

'An ending to my memoirs. I'll let you know. I'll tell you when to wear your legs.'

'I'll still see Andy. I suppose you know that.'

I'm not interested in this conversation at the moment – may never be.

'As long as you don't talk about him. I won't want you to mention Andy when you're bent over naked in the kitchen. That aspect of you is entirely unexciting.'

'What aspect's that, then?'

'Your feelings for Andy. West London domesticity. Your hair up, legs hidden. Putting Andy's dinner on the table. Yuk. It's quite a turn-off, that. You're quite unsuited anyway. He likes to eat out, Andy. A la carte, with a choice of wine.

'I like to eat out and all.'

'Don't be silly. Plus, he'll take you to the *theatre*.'

'I *like* the theatre, me.'

'Now you're being fucking stupid. You're a common-law wife from hell.'

'I love you too, darling. So – what will I get out of this?'

'Money.

'Ha! You haven't got no fucking money!'

'I'll scrape some up.'

She looks at me with dull uninterest.

'You'll be a piece of cake,' she says.

I'm quite excited. This, if it happens, will be the very opposite of boring. I'll get quite a kick from this, I think: being the only respectable old gentleman in the Royal Borough of Kensington and Chelsea who never knows when a passing sociopath in an anklet might put the bite on him. While others of my age and range of accomplishments snore the night away at a married distance from their wives – and with the radio alarm set for current affairs at 7 a.m. – I'll lie awake in appalled anticipation of three rings on the doorbell and the demanding arrival in my front room of Michelle and a posse of street dealers with their hats on back to front.

'Wake up, you boring old sod,' she'll say. 'We only live once, you know' – and suddenly I'll see the sense of this. There'll be altercations on the stairs and knife fights in my drawing-room.

So now I send her on her way – a toss of the head, a sociopath's skin-tight trousers, a common little anklet – and later I'm cooking in the kitchen (gloating, rather, over the size of the rocks forming in the spoon) when the doorbell rings.

One doesn't want chance visitors at such a time, so I avoid the mistake I made some years ago, which – but for the fact that policemen as a rule fall short of one accepted criterion of intelligence (an ability to hold two quite discrete ideas in their heads at once) – could have got me into trouble.

And that might be one for the memoirs, I think, if I can work out how and where to fit it in. Carly Simon had recently introduced me to Libby Titus and to Libby's boyfriend, Dr John, the distinguished jazz musician from New Orleans. One evening, when Dr John was in the recording studio, Libby dropped in at my place with a bagful of heroin, which was to be delivered later to Dr John. She had just put it on the coffee-table next to a large block of cannabis when there was a loud ring at the . . .

And it's curtains for this anecdote for the moment, since a loud banging on my front door suggests that whoever was ringing from downstairs has been let in by someone else. Then Pete the Schnoz, who is in Bangkok, starts to bellow at me through the letter-box. He's brilliant, Pete the Schnoz. He can sniff this stuff out from the other side of the world.

I'll ignore him, I think – but he continues to bellow through the letter-box, so, as a courtesy to the neighbours, I let him in. And we should do the whole lot at once, of course; pig out now and spend what's left of the night janglingly awake, staring skywards like dead men on a battlefield but with our brains screaming with self-hatred and remorse. Being in denial, however, we first act out our usual self-deceiving ritual.

'Just happened to be passing,' says Pete the Schnoz, a shade too loudly, rather too boisterously – and I've noticed this with Pete the Schnoz: when he's a little wired but, equally, when he wants to give a good impression (the impression that he's just come from a gym rather than from a crack-house in Ladbroke Grove) he tends to shout. He shouts, I'm told, when pitching a story-line to a roomful of money-men in Soho. Producers are a little slow but not necessarily as deaf as posts.

'Thought I'd pop in to see how you are,' he shouts at me now. 'You've sounded a bit odd recently on the telephone.'

This is hardly surprising. It's the Rohypnols, of course – not that I admit this to Pete the Schnoz. I sit tight and discover in due course that we've spoken on the telephone several times in the past few days; that we've discussed the *Root* special at length and that his first thoughts on this have met with my approval. Now, he's pacing up and down, eyes scanning the room, intent on one thing only. If it's here, he'll find it. I brace myself. This time I'll deny him.

'When are you seeing your baby?' he says.

'Tomorrow. We're taking Saffy to the pub in Battersea where Pratley plays the trumpet. He wants to meet her.'

'Aha!'

'What do you mean – aha?'

'You must have something.'

'Some what?'

'Don't be silly. Where is it?'

I don't know why he does this. I'd never choose to smoke with him. To me getting high is just a means to an end – a night of deranged, absolute pleasure with my baby – but for the Schnoz intoxication is an end in itself. He prefers it simply, and always, to sobriety, which is why his situation is precarious, I think, and why mine is less so. I only smoke with him because I'm afraid that if I refuse he won't want to see me any more. I'm afraid that the moment will come nearer when Pratley is the only person speaking to me; when I fumble with my change and become confused, irritate young people behind me at a check-out point.

'I haven't got anything,' I say. 'Honestly.'

He stares at me searchingly. All the resources of his enormous brain have been mustered to just one purpose; are engaged now on this single unbecoming calculation: how quickest to get me to concede.

'Promise?' he says.

That's extraordinary, but clever too. *Promise?* It's just a word but one which – in spite of everything – still carries with it a remembered load of honour. Penny knows this. When Penny is trying to get her way she regresses to the age of nine and, like a little girl trying to manipulate her father, she cocks her head most sweetly and looks at me from under bashful lashes and she says: *'Please. Please can I have another?'* And so I tell her that we've run out, and she says, 'Promise? Do you promise?' – knowing that for some strange reason (hidden deeply in the past) a father won't casually promise to his little girl the opposite of what is so. And Pete the Schnoz, who in his way is as manipulative as Penny, knows it too. I will eventually give in to Pete the Schnoz rather than bandy a promise trivially.

'Promise,' I say.

'I don't believe you,' says Pete the Schnoz. And then he laughs, because he knows he's won.

'All right,' I say. 'But we can't do much. It's for me and Penny tomorrow night.'

'Right,' he says. 'I just want one. Honestly. Just one pipe. I'm giving it up in any case. This is the last time I'll ever do it.'

'Of course it is,' I say.

And I produce the rocks from their hiding place and Pete the Schnoz snatches them from me and he tears them from the silver foil in which they're wrapped. And then he apportions himself a chunk which would drop a Polish docker and he puts this in place and he lights the pipe, inhales deeply and cries: 'JESUS FUCKING CHRIST ALMIGHTY!'

And then he falls flat on his back and says that he's having a heart attack.

He's as fit as a bullock, Pete the Schnoz – huge head, angry haircut, short arms, tree-trunk legs – but after one pipe he always goes down like a tent in a storm and says he's having a heart attack. So I ignore him now and I have a pipe myself, and suddenly everything seems all right. More than all right, in fact; it's as if one has woken from a nightmare, has suddenly discovered that there is, after all, nothing to be afraid of. And once I've got my breath back I decide to communicate this important idea to Pete the Schnoz.

'I realized the other day,' I say, 'how one could . . .'

'Do you mind?' he says. 'I can't speak at the moment.'

'You don't have to. I'm speaking.'

And now I can't remember what I was going to say, so I tell him instead about Carly Simon and about my evening with Libby Titus.

'You gave me a hell of a fright when you rang the doorbell,' I say. 'Worst fright I've had since Carly Simon.'

'What's she like?'

'Who?'

'Carly Simon.'

'Does it matter?'

174

'Of course it does. It's the sort of thing people want to know. You could say something indiscreet about her.'

'I wouldn't dream of it. Not yet. I love her. She's almost perfect. Very bright, very funny. She won't go out at the moment. She stays in her apartment twenty-four hours a day. She won't even go out to do the shopping.'

'Why's that?'

'She wants to be in when James Taylor comes round. He was recently cured by the Minnesota model. Twelve steps to recovery. All that crap. I spoke to her on the telephone the other day. "I won't go out," she said. "Why not?" I said. She'd just discovered that the twelfth and final step obliged addicts to apologize in person to everyone they'd harmed. "I don't want to be out shopping when James gets to me," she said. "I'll give him apologize all right!" Then I asked her what opinion she had of Linda Ronstadt. "She's a tub of shit," she said. Is that the sort of thing?'

'Not really,' says Pete the Schnoz.

'Oh. Anyway – Carly had recently introduced me to Libby Titus, who was over here with Dr John. One evening Libby dropped in here with a bagful of heroin. She had just put it on the coffee-table next to a lump of cannabis the size of a Cadbury bar when the door-bell rang. For some reason I answered the intercom.

'Guess what? It's the *police!*'

Pete the Schnoz freezes, eyes popping, the pipe halfway to his mouth.

'*Christ!*' he says. 'Hide everything!'

'Not *now*. In my fucking anecdote.'

'Phew.'

'Exactly. I ran back in here, snatched up the heroin and threw it out of the window, causing Libby Titus to have a nervous break-down on the spot – and one which she was still having when a uniformed officer from Chelsea nick walked in with my boy Charlie's suitcase. He'd left it on a train.

'While Libby spun distractedly round the room and while I, in my confused state, continued to roll joints the size of baseball bats, the officer methodically made out a form for me to sign, quite failing to notice all the other activity in the room. With one idea only in his head he wouldn't have noticed a dead body in the corner, much less a lump of cannabis the size of a chocolate bar and joints like dildos being handed round.

'After he'd gone Libby and I realized that the bag of heroin would have fallen into a small patio belonging to Lady Mallett, who owned the basement flat. We went downstairs and knocked on her door. She was holding an old-time dinner-party – suits, candles, conversation, all that stuff – and I explained that my fiancée and I had had a row, in the course of which she'd thrown her engagement ring out of the window.

'The assembled old folk very decently abandoned the *soufflé au saumon* and, with torches supplied by Lady Mallett, helped us to search the patio – but the heroin was nowhere to be seen.

' "Oh bollocks," said Libby, "I'll score some more" – and, leaving the old folk to continue with the search, we returned to my flat, where Libby was making arrangements for a new delivery when there was a knock on the door.

' "We've found your fiancée's engagement ring," said old Lady Mallett, handing me the bag of heroin.

'You'd have expected Libby to be pleased, but all she was concerned about was whether Lady Mallett and her guests had helped themselves to any of her stash – which, as I recall, they hadn't.'

Pete the Schnoz doesn't seem to have been listening to this at all. While I – quite adroitly, I think – have managed to mention Carly Simon he's been pigging the supply meant for me and my baby tomorrow night. Fearful that it will all disappear I confiscate the pipe, give myself a reinforcing lungful – and suddenly I remember the point I wanted to make.

'I realized the other day,' I say, 'how one could convey the effect of this stuff to someone who had never tried it.'

Pete the Schnoz – momentarily pipeless – has the deflated look of a man for whom life, suddenly, makes no sense. He looks aghast, like a man who has walked out of a big meeting, hurried home from the office and switched on *Neighbours* only to discover that it's an episode which doesn't feature Danni – merely the one with a big bum and lips like a rubber plunger. I ignore him.

'Most people,' I say, 'couldn't tell you if they're happy. They're simply baffled by the question. They might, if pressed, describe happiness as the absence of pain or any particular anxiety. They might cite small moments of exhilaration – you're offered a job, the love of your life is coming over in an hour – but they'd admit that even these moments are shadowed by a cloud of apprehension. The job offer might be withdrawn, the love of your life might not turn up, the cat might die.

'But on this stuff you *know* you're happy. Nothing can go wrong. That's quite a feeling to have. Equally, quite a feeling never to have again.'

Pete the Schnoz, who looks like a man for whom everything has gone wrong at once – who is already looking suicidal – stares up at me from his position on his back, eyes bulging with horror. He likes, quite unusually, to get the horrors while he's doing it. Most people prefer to postpone this dreadful moment for as long as possible.

'Oh Christ,' he says. 'You're not going gloomy on me, are you?'

And this is another thing he does. He accuses you of what he's about to do himself. He collapses the scrum and then accuses you of having done it.

'Certainly not,' I say, and, in case I refute myself, I take another reinforcing lungful.

'OK,' says Pete the Schnoz. 'Let's talk about something cheerful. How's your boy Charlie? Have you seen him lately?'

That's incredible. I don't think Pete the Schnoz is being deliberately hurtful, merely clumsy. Perhaps, being the same age as my boy Charlie, he doesn't understand.

'That's brilliant,' I say.

'Sorry.'

'No, really. You've cheered me up. Now you could ask me how my wife is.'

'For fuck's sake, I've said I'm sorry.'

'This will make you laugh. I walked out on my wife two days before Christmas. What do you think she did?'

'Look, I don't know, I . . .'

'She kept all the presents she'd bought me. She kept them for years – just in case I might come back. Years later I found all these presents, carefully wrapped and each with a hopeful message.'

'Christ, I've said I'm . . .'

'I found other things as well – hidden away, as if she was afraid I might laugh at her for having them.'

'What things?'

'Nice things, things for storing and transporting food, as if for a family picnic. Family things. She must have hoped that one day I might want to do something nice, like take her on a picnic. And I found a fondue set she must have bought. But she'd hidden it away with all the other nice things. She must have thought I'd laugh at her for wanting a fondue set. But she never gave up. For year after year she must have woken up and thought: Perhaps today everything will change, perhaps today he'll want to do something nice. I don't know. She must have been so frightened.'

'Oh shit, it's all . . .'

'Or you could ask me what happened to the chess computer she bought me to keep me happy in Ibiza. I was having lunch that day with Christopher Matthew, but she was so excited she couldn't wait for me to come home. She discovered where Matthew and I were having lunch and she brought the computer to the restaurant. "I don't want you to be bored in Ibiza," she said. She looked so happy, and after she'd gone I said to Matthew: "It's just as well she doesn't know I'm taking Melanie to Ibiza!" Eh?'

'OK. My fault.'

'Another?'

'I should fucking say so. So – why did you say it would be quite a feeling never to have again? What did you mean?'

I can't be bothered to explain. I know what I mean. I mean that the worst part of giving this stuff up – which one may have to – will be forfeiting this moment of certainty: the certainty that for the moment one is happy. That will be quite something to turn one's back on. It will be quite nasty to be aware that, however good things seem, there's something better. No wonder people who have given up, who have chosen sobriety, have an inoperable shadow of regret clouding the bonhomie and patter.

I don't mind for myself, but it hits me suddenly that if Penny gives up, if, after all, she chooses to save herself, she'll have to live with this for ever. In the middle of a dips party in the provinces, and while she makes a go of things with other disappointed women, she'll remember that there's something better: a place where it's always after six o' clock and nothing matters; a place where she could be herself.

And so she'll tank up with some more red wine (acquired by her discount-minded husband on a budget away-day on the Continent) and gradually the pain will ease. She'll hand round dips and circulate, and fat, respectable constructions will no longer make her want to die. 'Thank you, kind sir,' she'll say, and 'Such is life!' and 'To what do we owe this unexpected pleasure?'

And the image of Penny looking regretful at a provincial party, together with the slightly uncomfortable knowledge that I introduced her to this poisoned information, brings to mind another image on which, for the moment, I can't quite focus.

It's to do, I think, with a stiff barbecue party on a Cornish lawn, at which a police inspector with a hobby, played by a crap English actor, meets an offensively ordinary woman. And something happens, but I can't remember what. It's gone completely. A provincial barbecue party and a crap English actor in the lead and an ordinary woman and . . .

And so I have another pipe . . . and suddenly it all comes back! It's the idea I had for an episode of a humdrum ITV country cop drama. The day after the barbecue party Alison, the ordinary wife, is found dead under a Cornish cliff, and the Inspector, by unravelling her past, receives a valuable lesson: never assume that the defeated woman encountered on a provincial lawn doesn't have secrets up her sleeve.

It's an excellent idea, I think, albeit one which has slipped my mind since the day I had it. Well – not quite slipped my mind. I had another idea, I think. I intended to include a scene in which Martin, a television journalist who had loved her, reads an account of her seduction at the age of fourteen by Jake, the sentimental tough who had brought her up. And Martin, finding the unembarrassed simplicity of Jake's few scribbled pages rather more moving than his own self-conscious effort, gives up writing altogether.

Jake's account – had I ever got round to writing it – would have been quite touching, I think, and I can still remember some of the lines I had intended to include. Now, and perhaps mistakenly, I decide to try them out on Pete the Schnoz.

'How about this, Schnoz?' I say. ' "We left the girl under the shadow of the windmill. Then that joyful laughter. Now I can't remember it. Alison took her laughter with her." '

'Eh?'

'Sad, right? And here's another. "Is this how it will always be?" "Yes, Ally, this is how it will always be." They got that wrong.'

Pete the Schnoz, pipe halfway to his mouth, the lighter about to burn his fingers, looks seriously aghast. 'What *are* you on about?'

'Try to show a little interest. It's a touching scene from my TV series.'

'What fucking TV series?'

'I haven't written it yet. Jake seduces Ally, aged fourteen, under a windmill on the South Downs. It will be very moving. "Was there ever such a day, Marion, was there ever such a day?" Jake says that. Haunting, isn't it? Jake's as bewildered as Ally – more bewildered, perhaps. Perhaps she seduced him. She's very manipulative, Alison.'

'You've cracked,' says Pete the Schnoz.

I had failed to take into account his systematic lack of interest in my work. No point in telling him more about my episode of a crap ITV country cop show, so I have another pipe.

'What the hell are you doing?' says Pete the Schnoz.

'Having a pipe.'

'Fuck you! It must be my turn now.'

And Pete the Schnoz razors himself off a chunk large enough to knock a police horse bandy and he pulls deeply on the pipe, and suddenly his collapsed, clown's features reassemble themselves into a huge, life-enhancing smile. He's all right now.

'Here's the point,' he says. 'It wouldn't matter if the fucking cat did die!'

Nor it would. And so we have another, and then another, and soon we've finished it. And Pete the Schnoz cocks his head beguilingly – as cynically as an oriental cat, as wantonly as Penny on her worst behaviour – and he says: 'Let's get some more!'

'*No.*'

'Come on. Why not?'

'Because.'

'Don't be so boring. Where did you get that lot?'

'Michelle.'

'Ring her up. Go on. Let's get her over. She might take her clothes off for us. Do you think she would? Have you seen Michelle without her clothes?'

'Yes. No. She doesn't exist.'

'Just as well. She's bad news, Michelle.'

Not for me she isn't. I have recently discovered from a BBC2 nature programme how to protect myself should the need arise. The mistake antelopes make is to run away from predators. If they stayed put, a lion or a leopard would be confounded. They wouldn't know what to do. According to BBC2, predators become confused if their prey doesn't run away. I explain this to Pete the Schnoz.

'I won't run away from Michelle,' I say. 'I'll stand my ground and stare at her.'

Pete the Schnoz is quite derisive. 'It won't work,' he says. 'You've forgotten that she knows ju-jitsu. She'll draw you in, unbalance you, create interest where there isn't any. You'll be sitting at home, dreaming about nights of happiness with your baby, and Michelle will ring. "Sorry," she'll say. "I dialled your number by mistake." And then she'll hang up. You'll be unsettled. You'll brood about it. You'll imagine her walking around naked in front of you. She'll have created interest out of nothing. You'll ring her back. You'll be done for. Believe me I met a girl once who knew ju-jitsu.'

'Phooey,' I say. 'Let's go to Happy's crack-house.'

And so we drive to Ladbroke Grove, and we buy an enormous rock and we do this too, and by midnight Pete the Schnoz is bent double with remorse. He appears to have lost three stone in weight and six inches round the chest.

'Oh Jesus Christ,' he says. 'when will I learn? When will I ever learn?'

Learn what? That there's nothing else he wants to do? He knows that already. I recently saw a TV show in which Michael Caine was interviewed. He stood on the balcony of his penthouse in Miami and he pointed to an identical penthouse in the distance. 'I've just bought that one, too,' he said. 'Do you know why? I can't see the sun set from this one. It's facing the wrong way. I can see the sun rise, but I can't see it set. So I've bought that penthouse over there. You can see the sun set from that one.'

Seven hundred duff films and this fucking idiot still has the energy to move from one penthouse to another just to see the sun set. Pete the Schnoz no more wants to see the sun set than he wants to pick the laundry up, attend a lunchtime concert or clean the kitchen floor. Pick the laundry up? Open a restaurant? Go to the theatre? Make seven hundred duff films? See the sun set? Every possibility is as boring as its opposite.

'We'd better work on *Root* tomorrow,' he says.

So I agree to go over to his place in the morning, and after he's dragged himself away I become quite frightened too.

I lie in bed, jaggedly awake, with my brain screaming shrill insults at itself, and I wonder, as usual, whether Penny and I ought not to give this up. Not so much for my sake, more for hers. Her liking for the stuff seems to be growing at an alarming rate. She seems unable, like Pete the Schnoz, to handle it. Once she's started she can't stop; she always wants more and the craving simply feeds itself. She makes insane demands at 4 a.m., accuses me of holding out on her and begs me to call up dealers on the other side of London.

And when I defy her, this demure girl who normally is as unembarrassing as anyone I've ever met, goes into a humiliating, quite embarrassing routine – endlessly scraping the pipe, recycling bits of silver foil and, naked on her hands and knees, scouring and truffling under the broken coffee-table for scraps and crumbs.

Nor is this the worst of it. Recently she has acquired the eerie habit of regression. When every other ruse has failed, she suddenly becomes a little girl. She cocks her head most sweetly at an angle, and she speaks in a twelve-year-old's voice, and when I reprimand her she says: 'I didn't mean to. I'm so sorry. I really didn't mean to.'

She says it over and over again in the voice of a frightened child, and I become quite frightened too. She's reliving a nasty secret from her past, I think, but I don't know what. Perhaps it's to do with childhood punishments, with being dragged out of bed by her drunken mother and humiliated in front of guests – but perhaps she doesn't know herself. I take her by the shoulders and I shake her gently and I beg her to tell me what it is.

'*Why* are you sorry? *What* didn't you mean to do?'

But she just stares up at me with terrified eyes, and she repeats herself over and over again in the voice of a frightened child.

'I didn't mean to,' she says. 'I'm so sorry. I really didn't mean to.'

It breaks my heart to see her like this, and I decide now that, after she gets back from Mauritius, we'll talk about giving up the drug – or slowing down at least. Giving up completely might be dangerous for me. We were fine before we ever did it – witty and resourceful in our erotic games – but she may associate me inseparably now with gorgeous discoveries on the pipe. If we gave up completely I might lose her – like I lost Melanie. Nor, on any hedonic calculus, does it seem clear that letting her go would be the moral thing to do. I know of no felicific calculus which would necessarrily judge her safety to be more important than mine.

And then, to subdue my fears, and because it's a big day tomorrow – working with Pete the Schnoz and, later, our night out with Pratley and Saffy – I take a handful of Rohypnols. And, happily, I remember nothing more.

Until today. It's Saturday today, I think, and my baby's gone away. Accordingly, I'm on Mauritius time, which means that it's more or less 5 p.m. for me but only 2 p.m. for those on British Summer Time. And last night, to ease the pain of my baby's absence with her fat man, I took another handful of Rohypnols, and now, as I lie in bed, the events of the last twenty-four hours have this peaceful, Rohypnol-induced, dream-like quality.

Working with Pete the Schnoz is, I can see, going to be quite a test of my patience but not necessarily unproductive. Asked to sketch our working relationship the inexperienced memoirist, or amateur, would, I suppose, lazily produce a picture of two inadequately imagined stereotypes.

One would be a square-jawed naval man with a schedule and a steady tread; the other, an insolent junior with a haircut, who, between naps and eating oranges, can come up with three startling insights before collapsing with exhaustion.

Which, judging by yesterday's experience, is more or less how it's going to be. I arrived sharp at 9 a.m. outside Pete the Schnoz's amusingly unfurnished flat in Ladbroke Grove, only to discover either that he was sleeping still or, more bewilderingly, wasn't there at all. I waited patiently for an hour or two, at which point he stuck his head out of a window and poutingly informed me that there wasn't any milk.

'I want some milk. *Now*. I can't drink coffee without milk. How can I be expected to work without a cup of coffee. Why isn't there ever any milk in this flat? It makes me really angry.'

I bought the milk and then Pete the Schnoz took up his position behind a snazzy little desktop computer.

'Smoking or non-smoking, sir?' he said – and then he rocked with laughter.

'It's a joke,' he said. 'Airline girls at check-in points aways say: "Smoking or non-smoking, sir?"'

And this, I think, will be a daily reassuring little ritual, one of our small private jokes, which I'll remember with sadness when they take my Schnoz away from me.

And then we worked for half an hour which was long enough for Pete the Schnoz – once he had told me not to interrupt – to produce an excellent idea. And then he said it must be time for lunch.

'I'm starving,' he said. 'Why isn't there ever any food in this house? It make me really angry. Why aren't you starving?'

We went to Mabel's Diner round the corner, where, not caring that the soliloquizing street derelicts and barking bag-women behind us in the queue were gasping for a cup of tea, Pete the Schnoz brooded over the à la carte in a way that might have seemed facetious at the Tour D'Argent. His order in the end consisted of such unusual combinations that our bill for lunch came to £7.89 – an unheard of total for two in a fry-up place.

'It's like running up a bill for £2,000 at Marco Pierre White's,' I said.

'I'd rather spend £7.89 here than £2,000 at Marco Pierre White's,' he said.

'I'd rather spend £2,000 here than £7.89 at Marco Pierre White's,' I said.

And then, because our table didn't suit him, a party of street derelicts had to swop, and then he got up and opened the door.

'I can't bear the air in here,' he said.

I got up and closed the door. 'And I can't bear not the air in here,' I said.

And I was so pleased with this construction that I jotted it down in my writer's notebook. At which point Pete the Schnoz said that nothing I'd made a note of so far struck him as very funny.

'The target never sees the joke,' I said. 'If you satirized me as a buffer trying to keep up I wouldn't see the joke at all.'

'In fact, that's not what's laughable about you,' said Pete the Schnoz. 'It's your appearance which is odd. Asked to guess who in here had written a book or two and was once on terms with Anthony Powell I'd go for the chap in the cravat who's come as Milton Shulman or the immensely fat one pretending to be Orson Welles. I'd take you to be the only genuine down-and-out in the place.'

That didn't strike me as very funny, or particularly accurate, and, assuming that we were going to work for a bit after lunch, I was disappointed when Pete the Schnoz paused on the way home outside Happy' s crack-house.

'What about a quick smoke?' he said.

I declined, pointing out that I was faced by a big night ahead – my last with my baby for fifteen days, seven hours, thirty-one minutes and eleven seconds.

And now, as I lie in bed, all this is quite clear in my mind, whereas later events – the night out at the Rat And Carrot in Battersea with Saffy and my baby – have only the substance of a dream. Nor is this surprising, I suppose, since the effect of Rohypnol is to blur the outlines of what is recent rather than what immediately preceded it.

Thus the last event properly in focus is our arrival at the Rat And Carrot. Thereafter my memory of the evening unfolds as hazily as a botched video recording – the sound and picture sometimes disappearing altogether.

Saffy was looking lovely – turned out as if for a photo opportunity and with the unnatural, centrefold's bloom which one had always supposed was the upshot only of the latest studio technology – or applied after the event, perhaps, in a laboratory. She was flawless and yet, compared to my baby, as innocent as a May morning in a peach dress by Agnès B and with her little hands clasped in her lap – how laughably unprovocative Saffy was. The comparison, I thought, was between a real woman with secret intentions up her sleeve and something acquired in an adult shop to be inflated later.

Then there is a fuzzy image of Pratley, playing the trumpet with his combo, and mainly for the benefit of Saffy. He was wasting his time, of course. It's not Saffy's thing to respond – that's not what she does. Saffy puts out satirically, she instigates – that's what she thinks she's for. She's too incurious to respond. She gives out messages which she herself doesn't understand. In private she might pout and wiggle for a while, she might lie on the floor with her legs in the air to demonstrate an exercise from her new aerobics video. But in no time – unless she was in front of a camera, unless there was a release form to be signed and, in due course, an invoice to be rendered – she'd become confused. She'd grow distracted, talk about the cat, burst into tears.

Odd, then, that at some point in the evening I was alone in my flat, I think, with Saffy. I lie in bed and concentrate trying to subdue, and put in their proper order, the various particles of the evening which are flying around in my brain without cause of effect, as in quantum theory.

I do remember this: Pratley was playing the trumpet; Saffy, who had drunk a bit too much, was being quite amusing; my baby was as distantly, as enigmatically, in control as an oriental cat; and I was as pleased as Punch. Then Saffy said: 'As it happens, I quite fancy your baby.'

This is the sort of thing Saffy says, the sort of thing she thinks she ought to say, and I should – politely – have ignored her.

Instead, I paid the bill, waved to Pratley on his podium and managed somehow to get Saffy and my baby back to my place.

And then my baby startled me by saying that she had to leave almost immediately. She had to get up very early in the morning, she said, since she and her fat man were flying to Mauritius at some unearthly hour. I protested a bit, I think, but my baby cleverly won me round by producing a piece of paper on which she had adorably posted an agenda of what was permissable in her absence. So I folded her in my arms and I told her how much I loved her, and shortly thereafter she made her usual graceful exit – leaving me alone with Saffy the Page Three Scorcher.

And the next bit's very hazy. Saffy seemed quite comfortable, I think, and sooner or later she said she wanted to go on the game. She said she thought it would release her. She'd be able to indulge her fantasies. She wasn't really inhibited, she said. She just needed an excuse, a cover, a pseudonym, perhaps.

I knew exactly how she felt. I couldn't, under my own name, have called Barclay the Banker a disgrace and then kicked him round the room. I had only been able to do it as someone else. I, of all people, should have been able to find the right words to reassure her. I should have said: 'The sooner the better, it's your only chance,' instead of which I heard myself saying all the wrong things. I said it was an absurd idea. She should have more self-respect, I said. She was far too beautiful, far too special, to go on the game.

'Well, I want to,' she said. 'Shall I show you an exercise from my latest aerobics video?'

It seemed that I was to get a second chance. Saffy might be a performing woman after all. She lay on the floor and her skirt rode up her brown extended legs, revealing a parodically skimpy G-string tight and bright and *white* against her soft brown buttery thighs. So she'd got that bit right, she'd learnt 'the underwear knowledge' from Nicola Six and, as a consequence, I was about to be unfaithful to my baby. Nor could small shafts of guilt survive against two thoughts experienced simultaneously: I didn't want Saffy in the least (what was about to happen would be as meaningless as the hotel room fumblings my baby would shortly be enduring in Mauritius and, therefore, no sort of betrayal) and I realized, too, that this was exactly what my clever baby had intended. She had left early just *because* she wanted me to be trivially unfaithful to her. She wanted me, after she returned from Mauritius, to taunt her with this amusing infidelity, to ignite her with it in one of our sophisticated games. I mustn't let her down.

Then Saffy, becoming bored, I suppose, with her exercises on the floor, came and sat next to me on the sofa. And this was a mistake. A practised non-civilian – my baby, say, or, before her, Melanie – would have known instinctively that I needed her to perform for longer at a taunting distance; that she was obliged languidly to objectify herself, gradually to reveal glimpses of herself grossly naked amid the everyday surrounding hardware. A practised exhibitionist wouldn't have set us up awkwardly like two gauche twentysomethings about to grope each other on a divan. Never mind. I took her hand and she moved a little closer, and she said that no one cared about her and she started to cry. Only the cat cared about her, she said.

I did what I could. I put my arm around her, and she stopped crying and one of my hands had settled unalarmingly on a satiny soft thigh when Pratley, looking rather mad, suddenly arrived and whisked her off the premises.

And now, since I'm on Mauritius time, I realize I can stay in bed for another five hours and still be contemporaneous more or less with those on British Summer Time. It isn't, after all, as if I'll have a lot to do while my baby's in Mauritius. Merely think about my memoirs and work with Pete the Schnoz – and that latter activity won't be too taxing if yesterday was anything to go by. Half an hour while the Schnoz has a couple of startling insights and then down the steps into Happy's crack-house. I wonder whether we ought to give Happy's phone number to Mark Chapman and to Central Television too? They'll want to be in touch with their investment.

FRIDAY 1.27 a.m.

So tell me.

'Tell you what?'

You were going to tell me something. Something important. I know you were.

'I'll tell you later.'

It is later. It's almost two o'clock. We ought to slow down. We'll run out again.

'So what! We can ring Jillypoo.'

At 2 a.m.? You're cuckoo!

'She won't mind. And it is a special night! I haven't seen you for two weeks. I've been good for two weeks! I hope you were good.'

Of course I was. I've told you – I only like doing this with you. I wouldn't touch it with anyone else. Would you?

'You *know* I wouldn't!'

That's all right, then.

'And you didn't do anything else bad?'

Absolutely not. I worked with Pete the Schnoz. And I had lunch with Little Jo. That's all.

'How is Little Jo?'

Lovely. But she couldn't understand what you were doing in

Mauritius. She thought I ought to mind. She couldn't see that there's a difference. That when you're working you're not being unfaithful.

'Did you explain?'

Of course. But she just can't get it. She can't see that the real you isn't touched. And after lunch she did get me the Stevie Wonder song I wanted: 'I Just Called to Say I Love You'. She wasn't embarrassed in the least. She walked straight into a record shop and asked for it!

'It reminds you of Melanie, that song. Is that why you were playing it when I got back from Mauritius? You were thinking about Melanie!'

Of course I wasn't.

'Let me have another! Then we'll ring Jillypoo again!'

No. Absolutely not. I couldn't face her at this time of night.

'Please!'

No. We'd never get rid of her. Behave yourself.

'OK. Sorry. So – what else did you do? Did you crack those things of yours?'

What things?

'I don't know! Those hidden things. Rude stuff in code. To do with your memoirs, I guess. Helmut Newton and the banker's daughter. Sarah and the Polaroids. Mrs Mouse. That stuff.'

You mean my hidden files. I did crack them, as it happens. You want to hear?

'You bet!'

OK. The solution came to me out of the blue. The first stage, at least. Then it all made sense. I was . . .

'Let me have another. Just *one* more. Then I'll be good. I promise I'll be good.'

I don't believe you.

'Honestly. I promise.'

Just one, then. So – I was waiting to see Mr Chillery and . . .

'What? Who's Mr Chillery? I'm sure I've never heard of Mr Chillery.'

He's the Official Receiver. When you were in Mauritius I had to go and see him. Not a bad fellow – a bit straight up and down, a local government suit, trousers too short, pens in his top pocket – but not particularly censorious. He didn't seem much interested in how my shortfall had occurred, but I told him none the less. There was something about the atmosphere at the Insolvency Service – the numinous presence, perhaps, of so many entrepreneurs in Carey Street – which brought to mind the Helmut Newton story in sudden detail. Are you sure you want to hear it?

'Hear what? Sorry.'

The Helmut Newton story!

'Christ yes! Can I have another?'

You've only just had one!

'Well, let me have a real whopper and then I'll be good. I promise I'll be good!'

OK. Here. 'Thanks to you, Mr Chillery,' I said, 'I've cracked my hidden files. Thanks to you – or, rather, thanks to the gloomy, offensively high-ceilinged foyer to these offices – I've remembered the Helmut Newton story and can now include it in my memoirs. Would you like to hear it?' Mr Chillery was non-committal, so I proceeded.

'Can I . . . ?'

NO! 'Some years ago, Mr Chillery,' I said, 'Helmut Newton was asked in an interview what the greatest influence on his work had been. When he was a boy, Newton said, he'd read a story by a German writer which had greatly impressed him. It was about a Berlin businessman who suddenly faced bankruptcy. He needed a million pounds urgently, so he went to a friend of his, a wealthy banker, and asked him for a loan.'

'*Please* . . .'

Which was not an option, as I explained to Mr Chillery, available to me. If he cared to read my accounts, I said, he would discover in the credit column the sum of £100 remitted by a Mr Barclay. Alas, this didn't mean that I could apply to Barclays for a loan. Mr Barclay wasn't a friend – merely a client of mine whom, when my baby was in Mauritius, I kicked around my front room with the assistance of Tracey, my baby's beloved.

'You know what businessmen are like, Mr Chillery,' I said. 'I'm told that John Davies, the ex-head of the Rank Organization, used to humiliate members of the board by telling them to swab out the lavatories – after which he liked to visit Soho where he'd be tied to a whipping-stool in a third-floor flat.'

'*What!*'

What what?

'What was that about Barclay the Banker and Tracey? You said you didn't see him. You *promised*!'

Nor I did. I made that up. I just wanted to see if you were listening.

'Christ! That's *very* bad. I need another now!'

OK. I'll have one too.

'So. What happened then?'

When then?

'*I* don't know. *Then*. With Mr Thing.'

Mr Chillery?

'That's the one.'

I can't remember. Yes I can. I was telling him about the Helmut Newton story. The bankrupt businessman asks his friend the banker for a loan. The banker agrees on one condition. The next day, he says, he'll be taking his afternoon tea at Berlin's grandest hotel. At exactly 4 p.m. the bankrupt businessman's beautiful eighteen-year-old daughter, dressed only in red high heels and a fur coat, must walk slowly down the long heavily ornate staircase at this grand hotel, move proudly through the room towards the banker's table, let the fur coat fall to the floor and stand naked in front of him. If she will do this, he'll give her father a million pounds.

193

'Goodness.'

Right. Mr Chillery was all agog, so I proceeded.

'Can I have . . . ?'

No. 'The bankrupt businessman,' I said, 'who cherished his daughter above all else, was thrown into a turmoil of indecision. Eventually, unable to face ruin, he asked his daughter if she would do this thing. She turned her back and left without a word, but the next day at four o'clock she went to the hotel and she walked proudly between the industrialists and their heavy-featured wives taking tea. And she paused at the banker's table and she let the fur coat fall to the ground and she stood naked in front of him. He didn't touch her, and the next day he gave her father a million pounds. Helmut Newton explained in the magazine interview that he'd been photographing this scene ever since.' What do you make of that?

'Sorry?'

Explains everything, right?

'Does it?'

That's what Mr Chillery said. So I told him. The story, I said, was a clue to all the other stuff in my hidden files. All the references to civilians and performing women. The question of who's exploited in such a situation – the businessman's daughter or her father's friend the banker? Who has the real power? The spectator or the model? They're about the need for the protective covering of a *transaction*; about voyeurism and separation; about Saffy's fantasy of being on the game; about love and Mrs Mouse and Sarah and the Polaroids and Jacqui the Dancer and Carly Simon and . . .

'I know what! We could get Jillypoo to put it in a minicab!'

That's not what Mr Chillery said. On the contrary, he was most interested in what I had to tell him. So, sitting there in the offices of the Insolvency Service, I opened up the whole bag of tricks.

'Thanks to you, Mr Chillery,' I said, 'I now understand everything in my hidden files and can complete my memoirs. So – the next reference was, I think, to Annie Ross and driving with her to

London Airport. On the way she switched on the car radio and . . .'

'If we do it by minicab we won't have to see Jillypoo again! She can send the stuff over in a cab and we'll send the cab back with the money! She'll agree to that!'

No.

'*Please*. It *is* my last night back.'

No. For the last time, *no!*

'*Please*.'

And then you'll be good? You *promise* to be good?

'I promise.'

Oh fuck. All right. I'll ring her. I'll see what she says.

'Brilliant . . .!'

Lunch with my best friend Little Jo. She's so sweet. She reminds me with her radiance, with her received sense of a life properly to be led, of how things were supposed to be, but can't be now: a life of significant connections, not a game of deranged consequences with disjointed entries every time the page is folded over. Without Little Jo, I don't know what I'd do. As long as Little Jo says she loves me I feel I'm safe. Now she talks about my baby and asks me how long she's been away.

'Thirteen days, five hours, twenty-two minutes and seven seconds.'

Little Jo sighs happily and says: 'I *love* it when you say that! You really adore her, don't you?'

'I dote on her. There's nothing else.'

'Do you still keep everything her little hands have touched? Say you do. I love to hear you say it. It makes me all squirmy inside!'

'*Everything*. I can't bear to wash a glass if her little hands have touched it.'

'Oh God I love it!'

'I keep every piece of paper that once wrapped some sweet and thoughtful gift. I can't bear to throw away a piece of paper which her little hands have touched. She once brought me some blackberries she'd picked with her little hands. I've still got the carton she'd put them in. But my most cherished possession is some sand she collected for me in the Seychelles. Until the sand blows away she'll be mine, I think. Is that silly? Do you want to be sick?'

'God no. It isn't silly. I *love* it!'

'That's all right, then. As long as *you* don't think it's silly I feel I'm OK. I'm not mad after all, I think.'

'You're not mad. But don't you mind her being away?'

'Not really. At least I know she's behaving herself. In London, I can't be sure.'

And this, finally, is too much for Little Jo. 'How can you *say* that? She's with a man!'

'Only her fat man from Cornwall. She's acting. If she was with Tracey that would unsettle me. I wouldn't allow that.'

Little Jo shakes her head in disbelief. I've lost her. This she'll never understand. Little Jo, being normal, wants to be loved. She measures the value of her relationships by how much her 'boy', as she always calls him, loves her.

'I believe my boy really loves me,' she says.

I suppose this is how it should be. I don't know. I don't want to be loved. I want to love – *theatrically*. Love is a creative act, an art form. How can it be controlled unless it's first invented? The beloved must be perfect – obviously – and therefore imagined, a work of fiction. It doesn't just happen, of course, this way of understanding love, it isn't 'given' on the road to Damascus. You need months of instruction from someone already ordained in this mystery, and, finally, it's an act of faith – like belief in God or a particular football team. And then, like belief in God, or any other saving delusion, you cling to it, you carry out its rituals, its daily obeisances and acts of worship, because the opposite frightens you too much. You'll be faithful to your invention.

I don't pursue the matter with Little Jo, and after lunch she pops into a record shop and, as bold as brass, asks for Stevie Wonder's hit single 'I Just Called to Say I Love You'. She's a little confused, I think, when she asks me why I want it and I tell her that it reminds me of Melanie and her trips to Ibiza in 1985.

'I may mention her in my memoirs,' I say, 'and I want to discover whether my feelings for her hurt by being over.'

And when I get home I roll a joint from the grass that Jillypoo had left behind and I sit back and listen to the tape – allow memories to wash around me like the warm beach sea at Salinas, where Melanie, to my mortification, had played dolphins in the surf with Tanit the Island God, her fears temporarily forgotten.

'I met this guy the other day, OK?' she said. 'He was old, right? He was from the sixties, I guess. He carries a gun, this guy I met the other day. I'm quite turned on by guns. I think you should know that. He's a mercenary. No he isn't. He works for Metal Box. Anyway, he's left his wife and now he lives in a one-room flat surrounded by carrier-bags. He's got a trust fund, of course, which allows him to see girls and that.'

What was she talking about?

What *are* you talking about?

'I thought it was sad. I thought it might happen to you. I thought you might end up in a one-room flat with all your possessions in a carrier-bag. I don't think you're very happy. Sorry.'

I suddenly felt a little tired – I do remember that. I drew back and smiled sardonically, suggesting that this uneducated girl from Harlow New Town had missed a few levels of irony in the way I present myself.

Now I get up and rewind Mr Wonder, listen to this song again and sink once more into painful reminiscence. Poor Melanie. She'd been so brave but in the end not brave enough; she'd run out of courage, allowed herself to be broken by vindictive Christians in a seaside clinic.

And in Ibiza once I told her that she reminded me of Mrs Mouse.

'Hey – my husband called me Mrs Mouse! He was Mafia.'

Of course he was. Anyway – women didn't care for Mrs Mouse. They resented her excellence at play, her ability to make silly men feel confident.

'I think I'll go to the toilet.'

Don't say toilet.

'What should I say?'

Lavatory.

'Goodness! What else shouldn't I say?'

Pardon. Phone. Perfume. Mirror.

Look, I'm telling you about Mrs Mouse. Spontaneity and negligence, those were her areas of expertise. No code, only instincts, and sudden passions suddenly over. Everything on the spur of the moment – sleep, food, sex, friendship, kindness – everything suddenly or not at all. You're definitely a Mrs Mouse.

Melanie looked at me with dumb defiance, I remember – an expression Mrs Mouse had worn a thousand times when cornered.

'Who *called* her Mrs Mouse? *You* did. How did you expect her to be? I *am* going to the toilet.'

Lavatory.

'Fuck you!'

She was back in a minute with shining eyes and her head held high. Whatever she'd taken had certainly worked.

'I know what I'll do! I'll draw you a picture.'

She scribbled briefly on a napkin, then handed me the result. It was startlingly pornographic and quite accomplished.

'Is that good or what? I went to art school. No I didn't. But I could have been an artist. Don't laugh. You should know better than to laugh at me. I left school at sixteen. I didn't have a proper education.'

You shouldn't tell everyone. They'd never guess.

I said this a little more coldly than I'd intended, but I was upset still by her suggestion that I might end up like the man from

Metal Box, adrift with my carrier-bags in Fulham.

She looked confused, drew back, covered the hurt with a phoney smile. At Winchester, there'd been a difficult little boy who would never go down from a Bross Blow, who would never show that he was hurt. He'd bite his lip and wear a goofy grin, but he wouldn't go down. Melanie reminded me of that difficult little boy. She was hurt, but she wouldn't go down. I felt a small kick of pleasure. She'd mind her tongue in future. She might be pretty, but I could spit.

And now, feeling pleasantly sad (not because thoughts of Melanie had upset me, but because they hadn't) and meaning to get my writer's notebook from the literary room, I move unsteadily in that direction, and I spot Melanie's file (unopened now for at least six years) and I return with it to the sitting-room.

And thinking that the accumulated evidence might nudge me further into sadness, I open it up and remove the contents, and in no time memories are piled high on the coffee-table: letters, photographs – one, tanned and happy in Ibiza, another, as pale as a ghost and terrified the day I put her in the clinic – small silly mementoes to be kept for ever (shells collected on Salinas) and sweet little misspelt notes. One, left behind after her first visit to Ibiza, was signed: 'With love from your Princess for ever', and underneath there's a heart with an arrow through it, and a PS that says: 'Do you have a toilet handy and a mirror? And where's the fucking phone? I want to call Utopia!'

And I feel nothing. I thought she was irreplaceable and now these photographs could be of someone I never knew, the sweet misspelt notes could have come from anyone.

I find this very painful. An experience is meaningless, surely, it might as well not have happened, if the memory of it no longer hurts. Perhaps I'm not trying hard enough. I roll another joint, rewind Mr Wonder, summon up old Larkin. I get up and walk around, start to recite out loud – with resonance, with feeling.

'Can denial of you duck and run/Stay out of sight and double round/Leap from the sun with mask and brand/And murder and not understand?'

Nothing. I still feel nothing. So I recite it again, this time falling over the coffee-table and breaking it in two. I have to start again, feeling rather silly, even though no one saw me take a tumble. And while Mr Wonder sings 'I Just Called to Say I Love You' the phone rings and I know instantly that's it's Penny – whose power *is* actual – back from Mauritius a day early.

'Penny! Oh Christ I love you!'

'How did you know it was *me*? That's so sweet!'

'I just did.'

'Why are you listening to that song? You've been thinking about Melanie!'

'I *haven't*. Where are you?'

'At Gatwick. We've just got in. I'm very brown!'

'Where's your fat man?'

'God – I don't know. I've shaken him off, I think. I'll see you later!'

And this evening I'm struck by a thought that seems to me unbearable. I'm thinking of Little Jo, who has never in all her life done a shameful thing, and I realize suddenly that this will avail her nothing in the long run. One day, as surely as the rest of us, Little Jo will be separated from everything she cares about, from everyone she loves.

FRIDAY 2.37 a.m.

'There you are! As easy as pie! What does it look like? Let me see! Let me see!'

Not bad. Very good, in fact.

'She's brilliant. Jillypoo. Me first! Me first!'

OK. Here . . . What did you mean when you said, 'It is my last night back'?

'What?'

Earlier. You said, 'It *is* my last night back.'

'I can't have done. I must have said my first night back.'

You didn't. Really.

'Well – it was a slip of the tongue. The excitement of seeing you again. Your turn. Have a whopper. Go on!'

Christ, this is the best, right? There's no feeling like it. You can't beat this.

'*Right!*'

You feel safe?

'*Yes!*'

I mean *really* safe. It's important.

'Of course I do. You know I do.'

That's all right, then. So – I was driving Annie Ross . . .

'Can I have another?'

Look – I'm telling you about my hidden files. Pay attention. I don't want to have to do them again when I start my memoirs.

'*Start* them? I thought you'd nearly finished them?'

That's what I mean. After I've finished them. So – are you listening?

'*Yes*. Golly!'

OK. The next reference in my hidden files – after the Helmut Newton story – was to Annie Ross. That had me baffled. Then, suddenly, it was clear. I let out a whoop of excitement in Mr Chillery's office, which quite startled him, I think. For a moment he supposed I'd discovered hidden funds, but it was even better than that, I said.

In 1963 I was driving Annie Ross to Heathrow to pick up Oscar Brown Junior. He'd flown in from New York to star in *Wham Bam Thank You Mam*.

Annie was fiddling around with the car radio and she suddenly said: 'Listen. It's the Beatles. They're quite interesting. They'll usher in something called the sixties.'

Then she told me that, to do the sixties properly, I'd need a Mrs

Mouse. Also, that I'd have to be adequately capitalized. Apart from a Mrs Mouse, I'd need a penthouse flat with a sauna bath, it seemed, and a wardrobe suitable for meeting people backstage at *Hair*. Bee Gees and so forth and queers with ginger wigs.

'But don't worry,' Annie said. 'The sixties won't start until 1967. You've got plenty of time to find a Mrs Mouse.'

I was quite upset, as I explained to Mr Chillery of the Insolvency Service. Here I was, in love with Jacqui the Dancer, and now I was being told by Annie Ross that I wouldn't come alive for another four years. I protested, but Annie insisted that Jacqui wasn't flaky enough to do the sixties with. 'Dancers never are,' she said, 'You'll need a Mrs Mouse.'

'As it turned out, Mr Chillery,' I said, 'Annie knew me better than I knew myself. She must have known about Sunningdale and Winchester and transactions with silent women in the afternoon. She knew about most things, Annie, having herself done the sixties in the fifties while touring America with Count Basie and his band.'

Are you listening?

'Of *course* I am!'

Good.

'Here. Your turn. Have a whopper! Go on!'

Perhaps I should. I'll need to be high for this bit. I may not get another chance. I may not be so high again – high enough not to be embarrassed.

'Goodness. Why not?'

It's just a feeling I have. I'm not sure why. Just a feeling. A bit like fear.

'*Fear?* What do you mean? What are you talking about?'

Sorry. It's nothing. Who's Jacqui the Dancer?

'The love of your life. Before you met me, of course!'

Just testing. Anyway – you'd have thought that if one woman could have fulfilled my every fantasy it would have been Jacqui the Dancer. I looked at her and almost fainted with desire. Nor, professionally, and as I explained to Mr Chillery of the Insolvency Service, was she an unaccomplished exhibitionist. She was able to prowl the stage as defiantly as anyone.

'Perhaps you remember her, Mr Chillery?' I said. '*Summer Holiday* with Cliff Richard? Remember that one, do you? She was one of the dancers. Not the fat one. That was Una Stubbs. Nor the skinny redhead – that was the producer's mistress. Jacqui was the pretty one, the one who could dance. And yet just because she was mine she failed somehow as an object.

'One evening, Mr Chillery, she became quite playful; she danced around a bit and suggested that I take some photographs of her in the nude. She took her clothes off and she posed casually and expertly, as was to be expected, but – just because a transaction hadn't been negotiated or tickets sold – I found her behaviour quite upsetting, quite unbecoming.'

Incredibly, and as I now explained to Mr Chillery, I was unfaithful to her the next day with Miss Adele – quite a pretty showgirl at Murray's Cabaret Club in Beak Street, whom I later encouraged to go on the game.

'Indeed, and in case you have concluded that I lack entrepreneurial drive, Mr Chillery,' I said, 'I would point out that I greatly assisted her in this endeavour, introducing her to Tricia Bell of Nell Gwynn House – herself encountered thanks to an introduction from Hughie Green. That's by the way, however. Here's the point, Mr Chillery: I must – just because a transaction was involved – have found Miss Adele a more appropriate participant in whatever adult games were fashionable at the time. So Annie Ross had got that right.'

Are you listening?

'Sorry?'

Are you listening? Or are you just quietly finishing the stuff?

'I'm *listening*.'

Where am I?

'Here.'

Not *now*. In my anecdote. Where am I in my anecdote?

'God! *I* don't know!'

With Mr Chillery of the Insolvency Service. *Please* pay attention. The next bit's very risky. I haven't previously attempted anything as explicit.

'Good gracious! You'd better have another.'

You're right. Here goes. Later, when I lived with Sarah, I always carried a picture in my wallet of Sonya Dean. Sonya was a fashion model who was brought to my office one day by the film director Tony Simmons. He thought she might make it as an actress.

A few weeks later, when dropping in one afternoon on Miss Adele, I was quite surprised when the door was opened by Sonya Dean, last glimpsed on the cover of *Harpers & Queen*. Owing to laziness, perhaps, or a temporary cash flow problem, she had decided to assist the ladies of Nell Gwynn House. I saw rather more of her after that, being very taken by her stories, one of which was that she had had a short affair with the painter Pauline Boty.

One morning, Sarah woke me with the news that she had been going through my wallet and had come across the picture of Sonya Dean. Sarah had quite a temper on her, but on this occasion she seemed confused rather than angry.

'Who's this?' she said – quietly, not threateningly at all.

'She's no one,' I said. I wasn't at all troubled. Once I had explained the situation Sarah would understand. 'She's a model, I think. She has nothing to do with *us*.'

'What do you mean?'

'I mean she's no threat to *you*.'

'Why?'

I still wasn't troubled. It would be easy to explain. Sarah would see the sense of this.

'Because she does the sort of things you wouldn't do.'

'What sort of things? I want to know.'

'Not the sort of things I'd want to talk about with you.'

Surely Sarah would understand? We *lived* together, after all. But she continued to press me – quite clumsily, I thought – so in the end, and unable to comprehend why she would want me to discuss such distasteful things with her, I told her.

'All right – she likes girls too. She had a fling with Pauline Boty.'

I assumed, of course, that that would be the end of the matter, but Sarah wouldn't leave it alone.

'Is it exciting, that sort of thing? Two girls? Is that exciting?'

It was most disagreeable discussing stuff like this with the woman I loved, but I admitted that, well, yes, perhaps it was a bit exciting – in an insignificant sort of way.

Sarah was very quiet for a while, and I assumed that she'd understood at last. But then she really shocked me.

'Why didn't you ask me?' she said. 'I'd have done it for you.'

'You?' I was so startled that I struggled to find the most reassuring words. They came at last. 'Why would I want to do things like that with you? I *love* you.'

Sarah burst into tears and climbed right down to the bottom of the bed, where, to my great bewilderment, she rolled herself into a tight little ball and cried for the rest of the day.

I find it difficult to tell whether Penny is listening to any of this. She's kneeling on the floor now, holding the pipe tightly in one hand – as an alcoholic, I've noticed, keeps a firm grip on a bottle of spirits – and, with the other hand, she's endlessly, lovingly, caressing the remaining rocks on the broken coffee-table into the most attractive pattern – as a gourmet diner gooses saved-up morsels on his plate. Since I need to unravel the rest of my hidden files before I start my memoirs, I continue with my story.

Soon enough, and as I told Mr Chillery, Sarah threw me out. Two days later I met Carly Simon, who was over here promoting a record. She seemed to be the answer to any sane man's prayers – funny, quick, erotic, extravagantly talented – and in no time we became engaged. She flew back to America, the idea being that she'd pack up her belongings and then return to London – where we'd be married.

While she was away Sarah turned up at the office one day and suggested that we try again. I stopped replying to Carly's letters, and when she phoned I told my secretary to say I wasn't there. I left her wondering for ever what had happened. Inexplicable behaviour. That's not the point, however – as I explained to Mr Chillery of the Insolvency Service.

'Here's the point,' Mr Chillery, I said. 'One night, before she flew back to America, Carly quite embarrassed me. She took a bath and then stretched out on the bed with nothing on. "What do you think?" she said. She looked magnificent, in fact, but I felt most uncomfortable. She'd slipped embarrassingly out of character – as I'd slip out of character if, when the time comes, I were to tell this story in my memoirs. She had assumed a centrefold's pout. She looked lewd and suggestive. "Did I ever tell you," she said, "that Hugh Hefner once asked me to pose for *Playboy*?"'

I told Mr Chillery how shocked I'd been. This was a woman I loved and respected, a woman I was going to marry. No doubt I climbed into bed and turned away, thought about silent tall women prowling a stage with nothing on. Carly had confused herself for a moment with a Helmut Newton woman, a woman whose business it was to do this sort of thing, to pose and mock you at a distance, to wear thigh boots and stand in the corner if you told her to.

'Am I right, Mr Chillery?' I said. 'You'll know how it is. You'll have stood a few women in the corner in your time.'

'But what about the businessman's daughter? It wasn't business to do what she did. And she got a million pounds.'

I'm amazed that Penny's been following this.

Are you following this, then?

'Absolutely. All the way. Surely the *point* of the Helmut Newton story is that the businessman's daughter *isn't* a performing woman. That's what makes it erotic.'

I'm thrown for a moment, but I recover quickly.

Of course. But the story's a fiction, and Newton's photographs are fantasies. *That's* the point. The tragedy for Wykehamists is that they try to turn fantasy into reality – but with the wrong people.

'Oh dear.'

Oh dear indeed. Unless he meets a Mrs Mouse, a Wykehamist is for ever at the mercy of a silent, contemptuous woman in a service flat. Happily, and as I told Mr Chillery, I met a Mrs Mouse in the nick of time. In fact I met her for the second time. Years earlier, when she was seventeen, she'd appeared as a bimbo in the first play I produced. She tripped round the stage in a tight sweater and with her legs all over the place. Mrs Mouse's legs had a personality of their own and they got her a lot of work. Not that she needed a lot of work, since the good life was available to her in any case.

'She spent more time than you or I would, Mr Chillery,' I said, 'flying round Europe in a private jet, piloted as a rule by a French film director, sometimes called Clouzot, sometimes not.'

Then, in 1966, she auditioned for the part of Lady de Winter in the Alberts' version of *The Three Musketeers*. In the intervening years she had become a well-known pin-up, a starlet of the sort one doesn't see these days. You could buy posters of a swimsuited Mrs Mouse in the Charing Cross Road.

Everyone wanted to fuck Mrs Mouse, and many of them had. It was the thing that came instantly to mind. I don't think I did, though – as I explained to Mr Chillery of the Insolvency Service. I don't think I found her that attractive – or, rather, so obviously attractive that, having met her, there was nothing more to discover. It was as if one had already fucked her. A woman's mysteries should be discovered gradually, the experience should be cumulative. Mrs Mouse was the opposite of the plain assistant you see in Kall Kwik and who, after six months, reduces you to a lonely fever of desire. I thought, even when I was married to her, that finding Mrs Mouse attractive would be in rather bad taste.

'The equivalent, Mr Chillery,' I said, 'of finding Pamela Anderson attractive.'

I was very proud of her, however, and greatly touched by her fitful attempts to make a go of things, her little darts at happiness. She was very bright, in fact, and fully aware of the joke herself, able, when in the mood (which wasn't often; Mrs Mouse suffered quite badly from depression), to parody herself.

After she auditioned for *The Three Musketeers* I asked her back to my place and we discussed the tour of the first play I produced, the one in which she played a bimbo. I told her that I'd had a distant crush on an Italian actress who'd come over here to play the lead.

'You'd have been wasting your time,' said Mrs Mouse. 'She was too busy chasing me all along the south coast.'

'Did she – er – you know – er . . . ?'

'Catch me? No. Yeah. She was OK, Patrizia.'

I'd heard enough. The next day, and although I found her too obviously attractive, I was quite pleased when I found her measuring my bedroom.

'What are you doing?' I asked.

'Making sure that my bed will fit,' said Mrs Mouse.

She put my bed in store and moved hers in, and then she went out to dinner with Christopher Logue and stayed out all night. I was a little upset, though I was unclear why. The next day I asked her to explain herself.

'Are you cross?' she said. 'I thought we were sharing.'

Annie Ross had got it absolutely right. The sixties were due to start in nine months time and here, clearly, was the ideal person to do them with. I'd do the sixties with a Mrs Mouse whom I found too obviously attractive but whom everyone else seemed to want to fuck. I'd have the perfect other woman on the premises. For a year or two I'd not be bored at all.

'Can we get some more?'

I'm so deeply absorbed in unravelling my hidden files that I'm uncertain at first whether it's Mr Chillery or Penny speaking. It's Penny.

No! I thought you were following this?

'I am. I'm riveted. So, were you?'

What?

'Not bored at all?'

There was never a dull moment, as I told Mr Chillery of the Insolvency Service. We were a little reduced at first, but then we had a bit of luck. Granny died in the nick of time, leaving me shipping-lines and so forth. Mrs Mouse and I bought a penthouse flat in the King's Road and installed a sauna bath. In the evening I'd come home from the office, tread silently up the stairs and, with pounding heart, peep through the window of the sauna bath, ready to be aghast at whatever erotic evolutions were unfolding on its other side.

In the first year or two of what became the sixties few who were celebrated for one thing or another at the time failed to appear on the other side of the sauna bath's door. The cast of *Hair*; Hunt the Shunt; the Drugs Squad; Natalie Wood and Fat Antoinette; Diana Dors, Jess Conrad; a Radio 2 presenter who later married one of Janie Jones's girls, first seen by him, through the window of the sauna bath, underneath the Emperor Rosko and his disco dancers. And many others – Australians, Buddhists, libel lawyers, strange minority women in ethnic dresses – all organized by Mrs Mouse.

Alas, and as I explained to Mr Chillery, I discovered soon enough that this wasn't the life Mrs Mouse wanted in the least. It turned out that Mrs Mouse was a civilian at heart, wanting a dressing-table and to give dinner-parties for nice people more than she wanted to perform on the other side of a sauna bath's window for rock musicians and her husband.

There was quite a contretemps, as I explained to Mr Chillery, resulting in our removal to Ibiza, where some sort of choice arose between opening a library with my books from Cambridge – thereby initiating a Leavis revival in the Balearics – and the purchase of a glass-bottom boat. We bought the boat, and while I toiled away to the north of the island Mrs Mouse was taken up by the Elmyr de Hory set, shortly coming between Elmyr and his young boyfriend from middle America, Mark Forgey.

When Elmyr committed suicide, young Forgey and Mrs Mouse were able to finance a comfortable lifestyle in London from the sale of Elmyr's better copies of Matisse, Duffy and Picasso. 'If you're interested, Mr Chillery,' I said, 'I might be able to get you one.'

'What did Mr Chillery say?'

I'm amazed you're still following this. Look at the amount you've done! You've nearly finished it!

'We could . . .'

No. Absolutely not. It's nearly four o'clock.

'Jillypoo could . . .'

No. Anyway – Mr Chillery declined the offer. But he got the general point, I think. He understood that Mrs Mouse finally let me down; that she failed as the perfect other woman. But she taught me a lot – not least that you must start with the fiction, create the life you want to act and then cast the other parts appropriately. Fantasy comes first, then you fall in love with the created object. It's an act of faith – like religious belief. And you must remain loyal to this fictional object of your love, this perfect other woman. Finally, you must live with her, rather than visit a service flat in the afternoon. Mrs Mouse didn't want her home to become a service flat. But she bridged the gap. She caused me to keep an eye out for a Melanie. And when I found a Melanie there was an end at last to this demeaning separation. An end at last to squalid infidelity. Melanie was the woman you're unfaithful *with*. That was the point of her.

'I don't want to hear about Melanie. I really don't.'

You've got to. I've nearly finished. You've got to listen.

'I won't. I don't like thinking about her. About what happened. It's sad. I want to be happy. Why can't we be happy?'

We are happy. And it won't take long. Listen – Melanie was the best. Until I met you, of course. But even Melanie, deep down, wanted an ordinary life, I think. The night before I put her in the clinic – as she packed and tried to keep her spirits up – she started to talk about the future, about long-term good intentions and changing our ways and growing old together. She looked so frightened. She was as white as a ghost and shivering, but she tried so hard to be brave.

'Poor Princess. Poor Melanie.'

It was just before Christmas, and she kept asking me what we'd be doing in a year's time. 'Next year let's have a proper Christmas,' she said. 'We'll have a log fire and a Christmas tree and we'll give each other proper presents.'

'*Stop*. Please stop. Really. I don't want to hear this.'

Then she told me that earlier, while she'd been waiting for me to come home, she'd been looking out of the window at the family living opposite, and they'd been laughing together and putting their presents under the Christmas tree. 'Why can't we be like that?' she said.

'*Please* stop. I don't want to think about this. Really.'

'We can be like that,' I said – although I knew we couldn't. I knew that she wouldn't come back to me; that she'd be broken by uncomprehending Christians in that vile seaside clinic; that when she cried and said she needed me they'd gather round like obscene priestly vultures and convince her that she didn't. A ghost of her might eventually emerge, but for the real Melanie the game was up.

'*Why?* Why did the game have to be up? It's not fair, I don't understand why . . .'

And then she really caught me by surprise. 'I know!' she said. 'Let's have a baby! I'd really like to have a baby. Would it be a girl, do you think? Would you like that? Would you like to have a little girl, just like me?'

I hardly knew what to say. Why would I want a little girl? I already had one. I had *her*. For one more night at least. You wouldn't make that mistake. You're my baby. Why would I need another?

And, thanks to Mr Chillery, I've at last deciphered my hidden files. So everything's perfect!

'Can we get . . . ?'

No!

'Perhaps if you had another . . .'

No. Absolutely not. You were going to tell me something. I know you were. Something good, you said. Something good for both of us. Tell me now.

'Later. I'll tell you later.'

OK. Do you feel safe? *Really* safe?

'Oh *yes*. Never safer. Is this how it will always be?'

I think so. Yes. This is how it will always be.

'Is that it? Is that how it ends?'

I'm so deep in reminiscence, here at the Ivy, that I don't at first register who's speaking.

It could be almost anyone. It could be David Jacobs, the fashionable solicitor, taken for £10,000 and later rebuked pseudonymously in a daytime flat. It could be Timmy Williamson who walked in here backwards with a packet of Daz and later overdosed on Valium. Or it could be Dilly Dally, who, unusually for a publisher, thought that books had value, helped himself to Lord Keynes's treasured collection and thereafter shot himself.

It could be Sir Donald Albery, who came to the dress-rehearsal of *Beyond the Fringe* and afterwards suggested that we dispense with Alan Bennett. Or it could be Ken Tynan who was always kind to me and once trod silently from vantage point to vantage point in Thurloe Square while his cool and lovely Kathleen was kissed on the lips by June Upstairs. Or it could be Michael Codron, whose job it once was to ensure that Jack Hylton didn't attend meetings with lipstick on his fly.

Codron went on to better things, of course, in no time becoming the paradigm of an excellent producer. Codron's commitment to the work in hand was – no doubt still is – so rigorous that he would cast, rehearse and fiddle endlessly until he was satisfied that nothing more could be done to realise the author's aims. My own preference – keen as I was to generate enough in management fees to fund my personal arrangements – was to have a full hand of flim-flam productions stacked up like aircraft waiting to land at Heathrow, so this habit of Codron's quite confused me.

On one occasion, he and I co-produced Muriel Spark's *Doctors of Philosophy*, and I was greatly surprised when Codron called a rehearsal two days before the play was due to close.

'What's your game?' I said.

'We owe it to Miss Spark,' he said, 'to perfect the production before it closes.'

That caused me to scratch my head.

Or it could be Bert Leywood, who once sat in a Sussex garden with his beloved Ivy but whom I moved into smaller and smaller offices until he had nowhere else to go.

It couldn't be Pete the Schnoz, however. In due course, and as I always feared, the malevolent Christian counsellors took my Schnoz away from me, and the image of my brilliant boy in bits on a podium in a seaside clinic (the same clinic, gruesomely enough, from which Melanie never emerged) can, when I care to think about it, almost break my heart.

Nor, I think, could it be the old manicured *farceur* from yesteryear, who, fatuously, is swimming here against the tide; who, instead of being abused by a scornful boy, should be at home screaming solitary insults at a daytime TV screen. The old *farceur* wouldn't, I think, in a sudden rush of courage, paddle across the room to speak to me. He'd correctly recognize that we were in rather different leagues these days.

But it could be Michael O'Mara, the brilliant young American publisher of *Diana – Her True Story*. O'Mara's a real man, like me, though slightly realer – a point he made one day when I drove to his office and discovered on arrival that I'd dropped the car keys in the street. I'd have abandoned the car and bought a new one, but O'Mara, typically, insisted that we retrace my steps, searching for the keys. I was impressed. This was a lesson I never forgot. The exercise took two hours; we were so late for lunch that we lost our table and O'Mara missed three important meetings in the afternoon. Nor did we find the keys. O'Mara had made his point, however.

Or it could be my Uncle Hal, on my mother's side, who, after my father died, told me that Svetlana Beriosova had thanked my father for a diamond bracelet sent backstage by me. Nor, I now remember, was Miss Beriosova the first recipient of such a gift. When I was fifteen I experienced the delirium of first love, but the object of my adoration wasn't a spongy girl met on a tennis court in Sunningdale – as was customary and encouraged — but an Empire Girl. The Empire Girls were a line of precision dancers who performed in a stage show at the Empire Cinema, Leicester Square.

Many people in those days saw *Singing in the Rain* seventeen times because they liked it. I sat through it again and again, waiting for the high-kicking arrival on stage of my tanned and often sweetly uniformed beloved. She might have been twenty-eight or so even then, I think, but in a tiny military skirt and sparkly boots she was the prototype for all the silent women yet to enthral me with their mysterious aplomb.

There was no one like my Empire Girl on the tennis courts of Sunningdale, so I sent her jewellery, and she must have been impressed, I think, since she agreed to have tea with me one day – a day on which, although it was term time, I happened to be in London. I had been picked to play for the Winchester Colts in an away football match against Westminster, so I pitched up instead at the Empire Cinema's stage door with an exaggerated floral tribute, thereafter escorting my beloved to a traditional Lyon's tea-room in Leicester Square.

She may have been a little disappointed to discover that her admirer was a schoolboy; still more so when the bonneted and aproned waitress, taking her to be my mother, I suppose, gave my Empire Girl the bill. Later, and because the Winchester Colts had been a man short against Westminster, I was carpeted by my house-master Mr Emmett and thrashed for immorality by Pode. This is the life, I must have thought.

I wonder if my Empire Girl remembers this. I never saw her again, but it would be nice to think that, forty years later, the memory amuses her. I can see her clearly still, blonde and tanned and because this, forty years ago, was *her* time to dance and display herself with pride, she held her head high, tilted it towards the gods and, in celebration of this one-off unexclusive triumph – being young – mocked them. Or perhaps I have seen her. Perhaps she has been the bewildered old woman fumbling with her money at a check-out point or queueing for her handout in the freezing slush of a November afternoon, and wondering how this had happened to her. Once she'd been this other thing, but memories couldn't save her now.

I'm glad, too, that I've remembered my Uncle Hal. Mention of him here gives rise in the nick of time to a banana anecdote, which will be suitable for my memoirs when I write them. Banana anecdotes, I gather, are more or less obligatory in memoirs.

Uncle Hal's father – my maternal grandfather – had founded the shipping-line Elders and Fyffes, whose business it was to import bananas from Jamaica. Most little boys of my age never saw a banana until 1945, but during the war my Uncle Hal was able once a week to furnish each boy at my prep school with his own personal banana and this, I suddenly realize, is the cause of my enduring confidence with men. It arises not from my mother's habit of saying I was perfect but from the fact that, as a source of bananas, I was the most popular boy at school.

'Is that it? Is that how it ends?'

It's the Publisher, back at our table after his meeting with contacts across the room.

'Sorry about that,' he says, perhaps mistaking my momentary unease for annoyance at his absence rather than surprise at his return. 'I spotted someone over there who's got a book in him, I think. If he has, I'm keen to get it.'

I now discover that the Publisher's contacts across the room are my friend the washed-up *farceur* and the scornful boy who's hitting him for lunch. The scornful boy, I gather, is called Adriano.

'A writer, is he, then?'

'Who?'

'Adriano.'

'Good heavens, no! He's in the music business. Surely you've heard of him?'

'Of course, of course. Why do you think he's got a book in him?'

'Not him,' says the Publisher. 'It's the King of Farce I'm after. *Pardon My Blooper! A Hundred and One Theatrical Mishaps!* An exhausted genre, of course – leaden *racontage*, as a rule, about long-forgotten names – but the King of Farce is just the man to bring it alive, I think. He's managed, as you can see for yourself, to keep up with what's happening now. So – is that how it ends?'

'How what ends?'

'Your memoirs. *From Winchester to This.*'

'No. This will be how it ends, I think. Something like this. I haven't quite decided yet.'

MONDAY 6.13 a.m.

'Were you worried about me?'

Worried? No. Why should I have been worried?

'Jesus, I've been out for an hour. I only had to get a lighter.'

What happened? Why didn't you go to Mr Amin? He must be open, isn't he?

216

'I couldn't. I owe him money. I couldn't let him see me. So I had to make this huge detour round his shop. I had to get to the all-night store twenty doors away via the Brompton Road. At one point I was in fucking Earls Court. The streets are a bloody maze round here. I kept running down residential dead-ends. I found myself in the King's Road at one point. I don't know how the fuck I got there. Anyway, I got the lighter eventually, so we're all right now. OK – where is it?'

Where's what?

'The stuff!'

There isn't any. We finished it.

'Don't be fucking stupid. It was here. On the coffee-table. That's why I ran around at five o'clock in the morning to get a lighter.'

Well – you shouldn't have been out for so long. What did you expect me to do?

'*You've* finished it? I can't believe this. No wonder you weren't worried about me.'

We can get some more. Come on, you miserable old sod. Cheer up! We only live once you know. I want some more. *Now!*

'I haven't got any money. I seem to have lost £300. 'There was £300 in this drawer last night.'

Are you accusing me? I hope you're not accusing me.

'Would I do that?'

Well, you'd fucking better hadn't.

'I'm not.'

I should bloody hope not. And it's time you got the coffee-table mended. It's been broke for a year, the coffee-table.

'That's good. I'm in despair. You've finished all the stuff. I haven't got any money. It's six o'clock in the morning and you complain about the coffee-table.'

How did it get broke anyway?

'I don't know. I can't remember. Something to do with Penny, I think. The phone suddenly rang and I *knew* it was her, back a day early from Mauritius. I ran to answer it and I fell over the coffee-table.'

Well, you want to get it fixed. So – what are we going to do? Are we going to party or what?

'How can we party? I haven't got any money. I keep telling you.'

No money. No drugs. I might as well go.

'No. Don't go. For Christ's sake don't go now.'

Well, get me some more stuff. Come *on*. What's the matter with you? Don't you want me to wind you up? Tell you who I've been fucking and that? I may have fucking black men in my skimpy little knickers! They may have been throwing me up against a wall. Don't you want me to tell you about it? Come *on*. Don't you love me? Don't you love me enough to get me some more?

'*Love* you? I don't even like you! I loved Penny.'

Forget the silly bitch.

'I can't. Compared to her you're nothing.'

That's not what you said. You said you got an erection if I was in the same postal district. It was the thought of my milky thighs, you said. I quite liked that. Yeah, I thought it was quite funny that.

'Fucking tragic, more like. With you I've unlearnt everything Melanie and Penny taught me. That it's nothing without love. You're sexuality cartoonified and therefore nothing.'

Well, thank you, darling!

'Excuse me a minute.'

What are you doing?

'Looking for my writer's notebook. I want to write that down before I forget it. "Sexuality cartoonified." I'll want to put that in my memoirs. Actually, you're worse than nothing. You're a poisonous joke played on me as a punishment by a malevolent deity.'

You'd better make a note of that and all.

'I already have done. With Penny it was real. Christ I'm tired.'

Here – what star sign was she?

'Oh, for fuck's sake.'

Stop swearing. It's bad manners swearing. Come on, get me some more. If you don't look after me I'll tell Frankie Fraser everything!

'You would too.'

You bet I would.

'And that would be the biggest mistake you'd ever made. You'd be in more trouble than . . .'

What! I'd be in trouble? Why . . . you . . . you . . .

'That's right. More trouble than you could handle. I know people who . . .'

Don't *talk* like that. You make a complete fool of yourself when you talk like that. It doesn't suit you. Come on. Cheer up. I'll ring Space. He'll give us credit.

'Oh yes? And next week he'll be round here hammering on my door.'

Space? He'd never do that, Space. He likes me, Space.

'Didn't stop him coming round here on Friday. Screaming through the letter-box for the money you owe him.'

What did you do?

'What the fuck do you think I did? I paid him. Seemed better than being knifed.'

There you are. You *do* love me. Come on. Let me ring up Space and then I'll put on the little Katharine Hamnett skirt. I'll show you my milky-white thighs. And my luscious bum. You'll like that.

'I'm too tired. I'm too fucking tired. I shouldn't have to do this. It isn't right. I want to sleep. I really want to sleep.'

Come *on*. Ring up Space and I'll tell you about Denise.

'Who's Denise?'

She's got a flat, Denise. She's at it. Ring up Space and I'll tell you what happened Monday.

'No. Put on the Katharine Hamnett skirt and *then* I'll ring up Space.'

Yes? You promise?

'Promise.'

Can I trust you?

'Jesus – can *you* trust *me*? *Yes.* Of course you can.'

OK. There. How do I look? Better than her?

'Turn round. Let me see. So – what happened?'

What happened when?

'With Denise.'

I'll tell you when you've rung up Space.

'No. Tell me now. Then I'll ring him.'

OK. All day in her flat she'd been prowling around after me. It seems she fancies me, Denise. I went into the bedroom to get something and she followed me in. Then she throws me backwards on to the bed. I think we're having a ruck, yeah, so I try and fight her off. But I can't. She's a lump, Denise. Then she tears my clothes off.

'Christ. What, all of them? You've got nothing on?'

I'm stark naked, darling.

'Christ. Then what?'

Well – she gets busy, doesn't she?

'And you're still fighting? You try and stop her?'

For a bit. Then I think it's best to concede, innit?

'This is all right. This is better. So – did you enjoy it?'

Enjoy it?

'Yes, *enjoy* it, for Christ's sake. Did you *enjoy* it?'

It was all right, I suppose. Yeah, it was all right in a way.

'Oh bloody hell, you're useless.'

Well, I've told you now, so ring up Space.

'No. Not yet. Stand over there. Bend over. Then I'll ring him.'

I can trust you?

'Christ *yes*.'

OK. There. Nice?

'Stand in the corner.'

In the *corner*? Why?

'I'm going to punish you.'

You fucking aren't!

'Oh God, you're too stupid to understand. You haven't even got the self-esteem to be a proper object. You're too fucking stupid.'

And you're fucking odd, darling. Why do you want to punish me? What's all that about?

'It isn't personal. I only wish it was. If it was personal it would be exciting. You're material, that's all. I need an ending for my memoirs. You may be the ending. It may have come to this – a sink of degradation with a passing psychopath. Trying to communicate with a cartoon woman who hasn't the sexual intelligence even to enjoy being raped by her girlfriend on a Monday afternoon. There was feeling in it once. With Melanie. With Penny.'

Yeah? And where are they now then?

'Defeated love is still love. "Hate's victory can't make it other than it was." Rushdie. You wouldn't understand. You're trash.'

Thank you, darling. I love you too. Ring Space.

'OK. I suppose there's nothing else. Pass the phone.'

That's better. Here – did I tell you? I'm going to Portland Friday for a week. To see my mum.

'That will be nice.'

Nice? Bloody boring, darling. I'll be bored to tears. I thought you might send me something. In a jiffy bag. To keep me going like.

'You're crackers.'

Come on, darling! Just a little bit of gear. A couple of rocks. *Please*. In a jiffy bag. Just two or three rocks. I'll go mad otherwise.

'I can't believe this. You haven't listened to a word I've said. Try to get this through your thick head. *I haven't got any money*. None at all. Not a bean. Can you grasp that? My wife wants the rent, the telephone's about to be cut off and so's the electricity. I'm going to be cold. Really cold. Colder than I've ever been. And hungry. I'm going to be cold and hungry. Really.'

Oh.

'Right.'

Does that mean I won't get no jiffy bag then?

'I don't believe this. You're incredible.'

Yeah? And I'm hungry and all. I half fancy a pizza. Why don't you get me a pizza while we're waiting for Space?

'Fuck off.'

Thanks, darling. Here – do you hate women or something?

'Oh for fuck's sake. I was waiting for that. A droning flypast of received psychology at six o'clock on a Monday morning. *No.* I don't hate women. I like women. You, God help me, are merely the fictional representative here of a long line of mute, defiant women. I want to line up all the silent women in the world and punish them one by one. It goes back a long way. Something to do with wrong rewards. You wouldn't understand. Take your clothes off. Stand over there.'

After Space has been. Then I will. I'll drive you mad.

'And what if I ring him again and tell him not to come?'

What do you think? I'll leave. And then you'll be alone.

'Don't fucking threaten me. If you leave now – that's it. I'll never buy you drugs again.'

Suits me. Bye, darling.

'Where are you going?'

Home. Home to Andy. I want to see Andy. I really do.

'No you don't. There's only one thing you want. The pipe. Space will be here soon.'

Yeah, where is he? Ring him again.

'Be patient. He won't be long.'

I do really need some money, darling. For next week. When I'm in Portland with my mum. I'll need spending money.

'Ask Andy. Why can't you ask Andy?'

What! I'd never ask Andy. That's not what he's for.

'I suppose not. Well – that's your problem.'

I reckon so. See you later, darling.

'OK, OK. Come back. I'll see what I can do. I'll find some money somewhere. You know what? You really are a cunt.'

Thanks, darling! And you've had it, believe me. Why don't you go back to your wife? She cares about you.

'I don't think she does, you know.'

No? Oh well. Never mind. So – where do you want me? In the corner?

'Something like that. A little sicker, perhaps, a little darker – if I can manage that without causing embarrassment. It's a year later and it's come to this: a chaos of debt and drugs at six o'clock on a Monday morning; begging an ankleted sociopath to show me a little ordinary kindness. The girl might be Michelle.'

'I'd gathered that.'

'What else did you gather?'

'That she's inherited the Katharine Hamnett skirt,' the Publisher says, 'but not the inverted commas – a suggestion that you've lost control.'

'Right. I'm quite pleased with it – particularly the moment when she says I've had it. In wars, you know, soldiers fight on with the backs of their heads blown off. They're perfectly all right until someone says, "Hey – where's the back of your head? It's been blown off!" Then they keel over. For many years I've been waiting for a bought woman to look at me and say, "Hey – the back of your head's come off! You've had it, believe me." I think Michelle might be gauche enough to say it. I think it's possible.'

'So what happened to Penny?'

'I never saw her again after that night – the night she got back from Mauritius – three hundred and sixty-seven days, three hours twelve minutes and forty-four seconds ago.'

It was horrible. I thought she had something good to tell me and I kept asking her what it was. 'Later,' she said. 'I'll tell you later.' And she couldn't stop taking the drugs. Every time we ran out she begged for more. By three thirty I was utterly exhausted. I'd had enough. I took a sleeping pill and went to bed. At about five thirty I woke up and noticed that there was a light still on. Feeling a little groggy I got up and made my way unsteadily into the sitting-room where I was sobered up by a sight from hell.

Penny must have searched the entire flat for discarded bits of silver foil, the bits you put on the top of the pipe when you smoke cocaine. This clean and tidy girl had tipped out the wastepaper baskets – leaving trash all over the floor – overturned the rubbish bin in the kitchen, searched under chairs and cushions and tried to pull the carpet up. She must have found sixty of these discarded bits of silver foil, and she had lined them up on the broken coffee-table in four neat rows – like soldiers waiting to be inspected – and she was smoking them one by one. She was getting some comfort from smoking bits of silver foil. And all the time she was talking to herself in this little girl's voice. She'd regressed to nine years old.

'I don't mean to be bad,' she was saying – over and over again in the voice of a frightened child. 'I don't mean to be bad.'

And after she'd smoked a bit of silver foil, she returned it most carefully to one of the four neat rows, checking that it was in perfect alignment with the others. I maintained a writer's distance, watched with sorrow for a while – and then she saw me. She looked up at me and her eyes were full of fear.

'I don't mean it,' she said. 'I don't mean to be bad.'

I flew at her and shook her, and I tried to tear the pipe out of her hands, and she fought me for it. She was suddenly very strong, but I managed to rip it away and I ran into the kitchen, where she grabbed it back. And, amid the upturned garbage, we fought in the kitchen – me and this demure girl who, because I loved her so much, had made me good – until I managed to get it away from her again and, at last, to throw it into the rubbish bin.

That shocked her into some sort of sanity. She slumped on to the floor and she buried her head in her hands and she started to cry.

'What have I done?' she kept saying. 'Oh God, what have I done?'

She was sobbing uncontrollably and, in spite of the state she was in, I wanted to be kind. I stroked her hair and I tried to comfort her. I begged her to tell me what was wrong. But she just looked up at me with frightened eyes, crying and saying over and over again, 'What have I done? What have I done?'

And suddenly I'd had enough. It was nearly six o'clock and I had to get some sleep. I had to frighten her into seeing the danger she was in – the danger which, thanks to her, we both were in. So I told her that I didn't want her any more.

She recoiled as if I'd hit her. All the colour drained from her face and she put a hand up as if to fend off these unkind words.

'You disgust me,' I said.

'No!' she cried. '*No! Why are you saying these things? Please don't say these things . . .*'

In my nightmares I can still see her stricken, tear-stained face, just as I can still see Melanie's brave, uncertain smile when I told her that I didn't want her any more. But that had been a game.

This wasn't a game, and I got no pleasure from it in the least. My baby had finally let me down. I'd taught her to be unconquerable, to be the perfect other woman, and she couldn't handle it. My graceful girl had become ridiculous, naked and crying on the floor. She'd embarrassed me.

'Just go,' I said. 'You embarrass me. There's nothing for you here.'

She looked at me with huge terrified eyes and said: 'I've nowhere to go. I want to stay here. Please let me stay here. This is what I want. This is all I want. Please let me stay.'

I was disgusted and excited. I pulled her to her feet and I dragged her, naked and crying, towards the front door, and I opened it and pushed her sobbing into the passage, and I gathered up her clothes and I threw them into the passage too. And then, as an afterthought, I fetched the sordid paraphernalia of her addiction – the water pipe and the used bits of silver foil and scrapings of ash and filth and pow-der from the broken coffee-table – and I threw them at her, and the pipe burst open, covering her with dirty water and soggy ash. And then I closed the door.

I assumed that she'd pull herself together, that some residual pride, some sense of who she could have been, would cause her to get dressed and drive herself home. But when I opened the door after a few minutes she was still there, curled up and crying on the floor, naked and disgraced and crying softly to herself. And when she saw me she crawled towards me and she clung to me, sobbing and choking and saying over and over again: 'I'm so sorry, I'm so sorry.'

And suddenly all my anger and disappointment died, and I for-gave her everything. I took her back in, and we made love, and because of what had gone before it was the closest to her that I'd ever felt. So close, indeed, that I was tempted in the course of it to break off and make an entry in my writer's notebook to the effect that we'd refuted Sartre at last: all that stuff about love being the most tremen-dous contradiction.

Sartre says that in the act of love the beloved *becomes* her body, and so loses in the eyes of her lover the subjectivity which defines her – which he wants to possess but can't. His desire will fulfil itself only by frustrating itself, leaving him with the freedom of the beloved still further removed.

I didn't feel that now. I knew now that I could love another with-out love's accompanying load of necessary hatred – hatred of the other's freedom. I could love someone now without sophisticated games and nursery punishments. The past, as a conditioning influ-ence, was dead, things were entirely what they appeared to be, and behind them there was nothing. I was free to be anything I wanted; best of all, there was no need to write my memoirs, and I said as much to Penny.

'Guess what?' I said. 'The past's dead. I won't have to write my fucking memoirs! Isn't that great?'

And then, by way of explanation, I reached for my pocket Scruton at the bedside and I quoted his analysis of Sartre at length.

And Penny laughed happily and said: 'I could have learnt so much from you. I could have learnt so much.'

I had the first inkling then that something might be wrong. But she snuggled up closer to me in the bed and she sighed happily and I was reassured.

And then I said: 'Was there ever such a day, Marion, was there ever such a day?' I don't know why I said it; the words seemed to come from nowhere. And Penny gave a little start, and she sat up suddenly in bed and, as she always did when something puzzled her, she frowned and put a thoughtful finger to her lips.

'Why Marion?' she said. 'Who's Marion? I've heard that before, I'm sure I have.'

And she started to cry again, quite softly, she just lay there next to me with tears running down her cheeks. And I knew then that there was something unbearable to come.

'What is it?' I said, although I knew. I knew that she had decided not to be fourteen years old for ever, not to be punished for ever by parents and surrogate parents for a crime she hadn't committed. She had decided, for whatever reason, to grow up. 'Why did you say you *could* have learnt so much from me? What did you mean, you *could* have done?'

And then, quite casually, she told me what she'd been keeping from me. She was going to live with her fat man in Cornwall. It had all been decided in Mauritius.

I should have left it at that, but foolishly, and as one does, I quizzed her. I asked her why – or something which was equally a waste of time.

'He's kind to me,' she said.

I haven't seen her since. I've spoken to her once. When Little Jo died I wanted very much to share this dreadful thing with her. Little Jo had been the best thing in the world and I wanted very much to share with Penny the injustice of what had happened. And so I rang her up in Cornwall.

'Little Jo died yesterday,' I said. 'I don't know what to do. Nothing will ever make sense again.'

Penny was silent for a while, and then, when she spoke, her voice was chilly with contempt.

'Don't worry,' she said. 'I'm sure you'll be able to use it to your advantage.' And then she put the receiver down.

The Publisher is looking a bit uncomfortable, and I fear I may have embarrassed him.

'Oh dear, I've embarrassed you,' I say. 'One so hates to embarrass people.'

'No, no – not at all,' he says. 'Really, I do assure you.'

But I've told him too much, I think, I've stood too close to him – something we were warned against at Winchester. At Winchester we were discouraged from standing too close, from making, or seeking, personal disclosures. The other day I met a fellow Wykehamist – someone I'd known for forty years – and after the preliminaries I said: 'Are you happy?'

He took a pace back and squinted with surprise. 'Are you pulling my wire?' he said. 'That's none of your business.'

At Winchester we were none of us each other's business. We cracked on.

'You obviously miss her,' the Publisher says.

'Most of the time. I still have the Polaroids, of course. Would you like to see them?'

"That won't be necessary,' the Publisher says. 'So – when can you start?'

Quite soon now. I've got some stuff to do, and then I'll start.